AS/A-LEVEL YEAR 1

STUDENT GUIDE

AQA

Physics

Sections 4 and 5

Mechanics and materials

Electricity

Ian Lovat

PHILIP ALLAN FOR HODDER EDUCATION

AN HACHETTE UK COMPANY

Philip Allan, an imprint of Hodder Education, an Hachette UK company, Blenheim Court, George Street, Banbury, Oxfordshire OX16 5BH

Orders

Bookpoint Ltd, 130 Milton Park, Abingdon, Oxfordshire OX14 4SB

tel: 01235 827827

fax: 01235 400401

e-mail: education@bookpoint.co.uk

Lines are open 9.00 a.m.–5.00 p.m., Monday to Saturday, with a 24-hour message answering service. You can also order through the Hodder Education website: www.hoddereducation.co.uk

ISBN 978-1-4718-4378-5

First printed 2015

Impression number 5 4 3 2 1

Year 2018 2017 2016 2015

This guide has been written specifically to support students preparing for the AQA AS and A level Physics (Sections 4 and 5) examinations. The content has been neither approved nor endorsed by AQA and remains the sole responsibility of the author.

Cover photo: Beboy/Fotolia

Typeset by Integra Software Services Pvt Ltd, Pondicherry, India

Printed in Italy

Contents

Getting the most from this book

Exam tips

Advice on key points in the text to help you learn and recall content, avoid pitfalls, and polish your exam technique in order to boost your grade.

Knowledge check

Rapid-fire questions throughout the Content Guidance section to check your understanding.

Knowledge check answers

1 Turn to the back of the book for the Knowledge check answers.

Summaries

- Each core topic is rounded off by a bullet-list summary for quick-check reference of what you need to know.

Exam-style questions

Commentary on the questions

Tips on what you need to do to gain full marks, indicated by the icon ⓔ

Sample student answers

Practise the questions, then look at the student answers that follow.

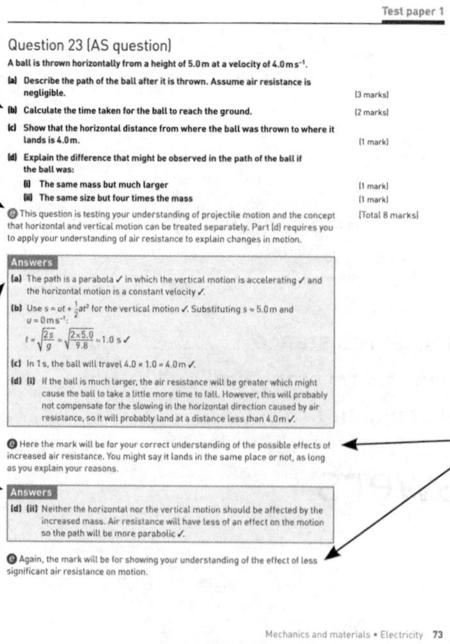
Test paper 1

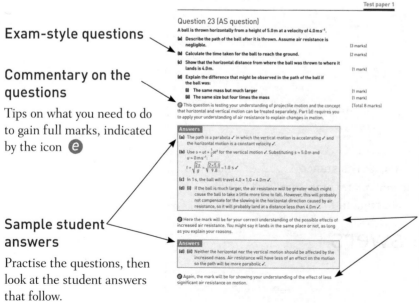

Question 23 (AS question)

A ball is thrown horizontally from a height of 5.0 m at a velocity of $4.0\,\mathrm{m\,s^{-1}}$.

(a) Describe the path of the ball after it is thrown. Assume air resistance is negligible. (3 marks)

(b) Calculate the time taken for the ball to reach the ground. (2 marks)

(c) Show that the horizontal distance from where the ball was thrown to where it lands is 4.0 m. (1 mark)

(d) Explain the difference that might be observed in the path of the ball if the ball was:

(i) The same mass but much larger (1 mark)

(ii) The same size but four times the mass (1 mark)

(Total 8 marks)

ⓔ This question is testing your understanding of projectile motion and the concept that horizontal and vertical motion can be treated separately. Part (d) requires you to apply your understanding of air resistance to explain changes in motion.

Answers

(a) The path is a parabola ✓ in which the vertical motion is accelerating ✓ and the horizontal motion is a constant velocity ✓.

(b) Use $s = ut + \frac{1}{2}at^2$ for the vertical motion ✓. Substituting $s = 5.0$ m and $u = 0\,\mathrm{m\,s^{-1}}$:

$t = \sqrt{\frac{2s}{g}} = \sqrt{\frac{2\times5.0}{9.8}} = 1.0$ s ✓

(c) In 1 s, the ball will travel $4.0 \times 1.0 = 4.0$ m ✓.

(d) (i) If the ball is much larger, the air resistance will be greater which might cause the ball to take a little more time to fall. However, this will probably not compensate for the slowing in the horizontal direction caused by air resistance, so it will probably land at a distance less than 4.0 m ✓.

ⓔ Here the mark will be for your correct understanding of the possible effects of increased air resistance. You might say it lands in the same place or not, as long as you explain your reasons.

Answers

(d) (ii) Neither the horizontal nor the vertical motion should be affected by the increased mass. Air resistance will have less of an effect on the motion so the path will be more parabolic ✓.

ⓔ Again, the mark will be for showing your understanding of the effect of less significant air resistance on motion.

Mechanics and materials • Electricity 73

Commentary on sample student answers

Find out how many marks each answer would be awarded in the exam and then read the comments (preceded by the icon ⓔ) showing exactly how and where marks are gained or lost.

About this book

This guide covers sections 4 and 5 of the AQA Physics A-level and AS specifications. It is intended to help you to remember and understand the physics you need for the course and is set out in the same order as the specification so you can check that you have covered everything. There are two main sections:

The **Content Guidance** section is not a detailed textbook but is guidance on the main points of the topics covered. It is intended to help you understand what is needed and how to use that understanding and knowledge in questions. The worked examples should help you to understand the principles and see the sorts of questions that you might be required to do in an examination. There are some quick knowledge check questions that will help you to be confident you have understood each point of physics. The exam tips give further guidance on core aspects of the subject and ways to improve your exam performance. Required practical work is also covered in this section.

The **Questions & Answers** section has two test papers with answers so that you can practise questions and see the sorts of answers that are needed, and the knowledge and understanding that is required. If you are taking an AS examination in physics, the questions will not be quite as difficult as the questions you will get on the same material for A-level. The A-level questions are highlighted in this section.

You will need to learn the basic facts and ensure that you really understand the connections between different ideas. It is often helpful to learn beyond the specification so that these connections become more obvious. The more you can do this, the better you will be able to tackle new questions or different ideas. If you try all the questions in this book and more besides, you will be able to approach any examination with confidence.

To help you check your progress, at the end of this guide you can find the answers to all the knowledge check questions in the content guidance section.

Content Guidance

Mechanics and materials

Force, energy and momentum

Scalars and vectors

Quantities in physics can be classed as either scalars or vectors. Scalars are quantities with size (magnitude) only, for example, mass, distance, speed, energy and temperature. Vectors have a magnitude and a direction, for example, displacement, velocity, acceleration, force, weight and momentum.

Vector quantities can be represented by an arrow with a length that shows the magnitude and a direction. For example, distance is simply the total distance travelled by an object. Displacement is the distance in a straight line from the starting point to the finishing point with the direction from the starting point. This is shown in Figure 1.

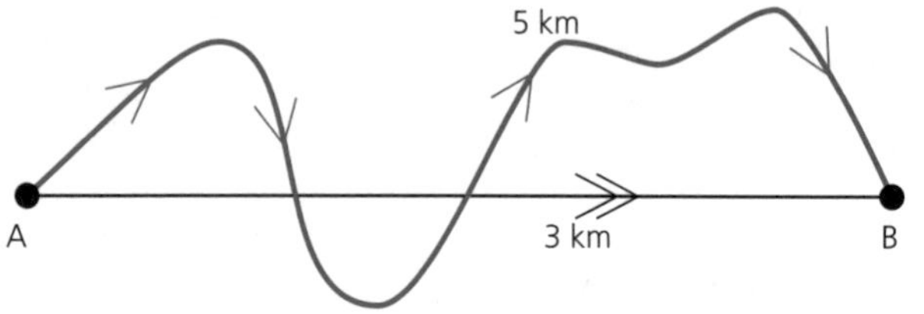

Figure 1 A walk along a winding path

If you walk along the winding path from point A to point B, the direction you travel in varies and the total distance you walk is 5 km. Distance is a scalar quantity. However, you end up at point B, 3 km from your starting point, due east of point A. Your displacement is 3 km east. Displacement has magnitude and direction, so it is a vector quantity.

If you took 45 minutes to walk 5 km, using:

$$\text{average speed} = \frac{\text{total distance travelled}}{\text{total time taken}}$$

Your average speed would be 6.7 km h^{-1}, and using:

$$\text{average velocity} = \frac{\text{total displacement}}{\text{total time taken}}$$

Your average velocity would be 4 km h^{-1} east.

Exam tip

Be careful to show or describe the directions of vectors in any answer. The direction is often given or implied by the question or calculated answer.

Knowledge check 1

Name five scalar quantities and five vector quantities.

Adding scalars and vectors

Scalar quantities are added or subtracted as numbers. For example, if you walk 5 km and then walk another 3 km, you will have walked a total of 8 km.

When vector quantities are added, their direction needs to be considered as well as their size. You can do this by drawing a diagram to show the size and direction of each vector. Vectors are always added 'tip to tail' and can be at any angle to each other. You will need to know how to calculate the sum of two vectors at right angles to each other or how to use a drawing to find the sum of two vectors at other angles.

In Figure 2, you walk 3 km due east followed by 4 km due south. The total distance covered is 7 km, but your displacement is given by adding the two vectors. You could draw the vectors to scale, say 1 cm:1 km, and measure the length and angle of the resultant.

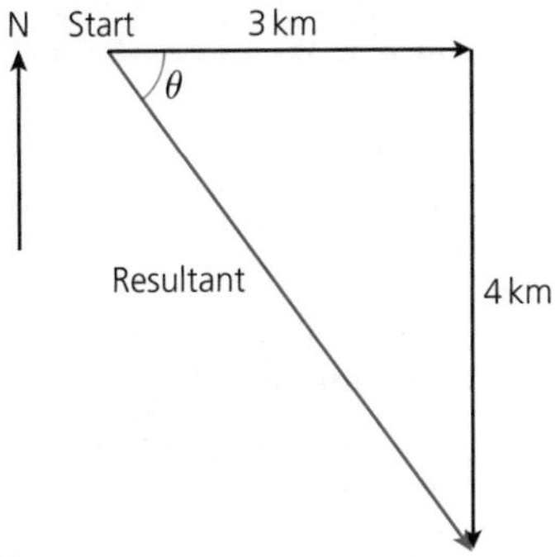

Figure 2 Adding two vectors at right angles to each other

Alternatively, you could use Pythagoras' theorem to calculate the resultant, which gives:

$$\sqrt{3^2+4^2} = 5\,\text{km}$$

The angle θ can then be calculated using:

$$\tan^{-1}\left(\frac{4}{3}\right) = 53°$$

Suppose you walk 3 km east followed by 4 km southeast. The diagram will now look like Figure 3.

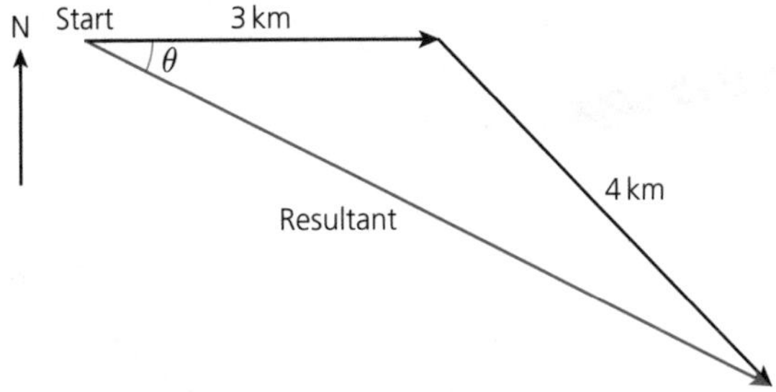

Figure 3 Adding two vectors not at right angles to each other

You could use the same scale as before and draw the vectors carefully, 'tip to tail' pointing in the correct direction. By measuring the length of the resultant and the angle θ, you would find that the resultant is 6.5 km at 26° south from east (or 116° from north).

Exam tip

Always show the direction of the vectors clearly using arrows. Use a ruler and measure carefully.

Exam tip

You can find the resultant of two vectors that are not at right angles by calculation if you know how to do so.

Resolution of vectors

A vector can be **resolved** into two **components** that are at right angles to each other. This can be a useful technique and is one you will often use when resolving forces.

Figure 4 Resolving forces

In Figure 4, the boy is pulling a cart along with a force, F. He is not pulling it horizontally but at an angle θ to the horizontal. The horizontal force, F_H, can be worked out using trigonometry:

$$F_H = F \times \cos\theta$$

This is the horizontal component of the force. The vertical component, F_V, is given by:

$$F_V = F \times \sin\theta$$

These two components, if added together, will give the resultant vector, F.

The components do not have to be horizontal and vertical. They can be in any direction as long as the two components are at right angles to each other. This is often useful when thinking about the forces acting on an object on a slope.

In Figure 5, the component of the trolley's weight down the slope, F_D, is given by $W \times \sin\theta$ and the component of the weight perpendicular (normal) to the slope is given by $W \times \cos\theta$.

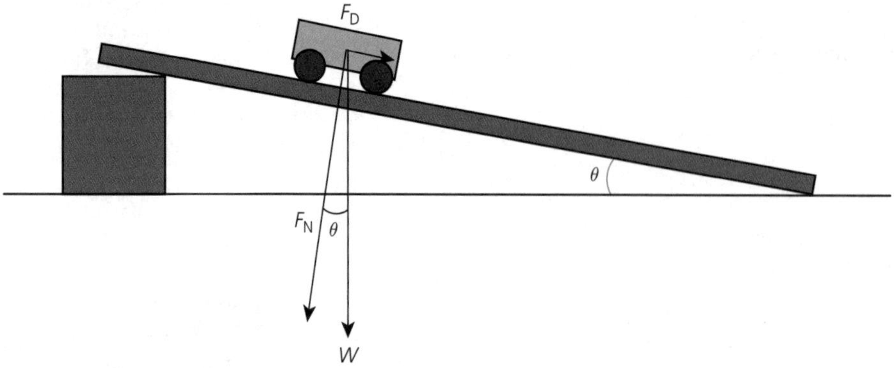

Figure 5 Forces acting on a trolley on a slope. The weight can be resolved into a component down the slope and a component normal to the slope

If you have trouble remembering which component is $F \times \sin\theta$ and which is $F \times \cos\theta$, Figure 6 may help.

Components of a force are two forces at right angles to each other, which when added together as vectors have a resultant equal to the original force. Any vector can be resolved into perpendicular components.

Knowledge check 2

In Figure 4, the boy pulls the cart with a force of 40 N at an angle of 30° to the horizontal. Calculate the horizontal and vertical components of the force.

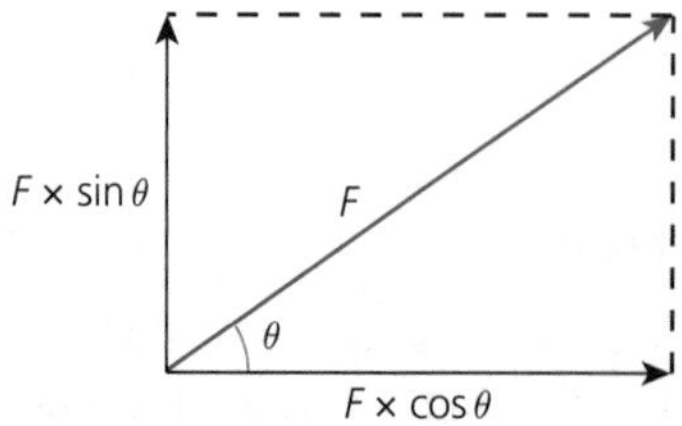

Figure 6 Components of forces

Objects in equilibrium

If an object is in equilibrium, all the forces acting on it add up to zero. The vector sum of the forces has no resultant. A simple example of this is shown in Figure 7.

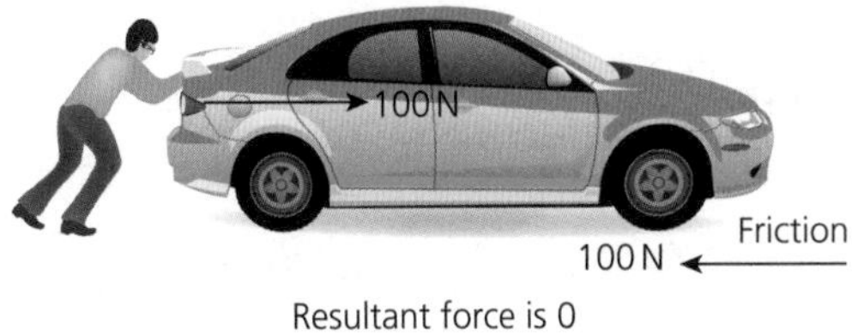

Figure 7 The two vectors are the same length and in opposite directions so when they are added together 'tip to tail', the resultant is zero. No resultant force on the car means its velocity does not change

If there are three or more forces acting on an object, the resultant can still be zero. Suppose three students pull in different directions on a ring so that the ring remains still. The forces must add up to give a zero resultant, as shown in Figure 8.

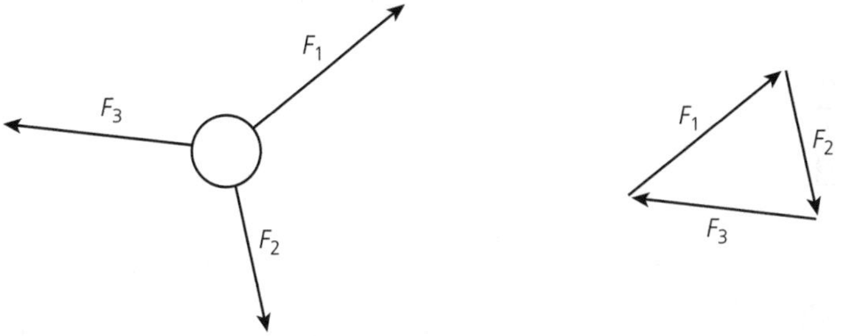

Figure 8 The three forces acting on the ring are added together 'tip to tail' to give a complete triangle with no resultant force. The ring remains at rest and is therefore in equilibrium

Knowledge check 3

In Figure 8, F_1 is 30 N at 45° to north, and F_2 is 25 N at 160° to north. The ring is in equilibrium. Use a scale drawing to find the magnitude and direction of F_3.

Summary

After studying this topic you should:

- know that quantities can be either scalars or vectors
- know that a scalar quantity has just magnitude and a vector quantity has both magnitude and direction. Examples of scalar quantities are mass, length, time, distance, speed and energy. Examples of vector quantities are weight, force, displacement, velocity, acceleration and momentum
- be able to add vector quantities taking their magnitude and direction into account. For vectors at right angles, you should be able to calculate the resultant
- be able to resolve any vector into two components which are at right angles to each other
- be able to add three or more forces to show that the resultant is zero and therefore the object on which they act is in equilibrium

Moments

Moment of a force

When a force acts on an object and causes it to turn, this turning effect is called the moment of the force. The moment of a force about a point is defined as:

force × perpendicular distance from the point to the line of action of the force

Figure 9 shows an example of this.

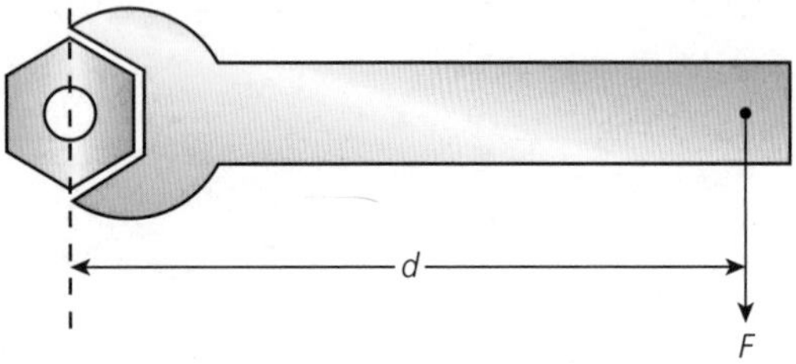

Figure 9 The line of action of the force is shown by the direction of the arrow F. The moment of the force is $F \times d$

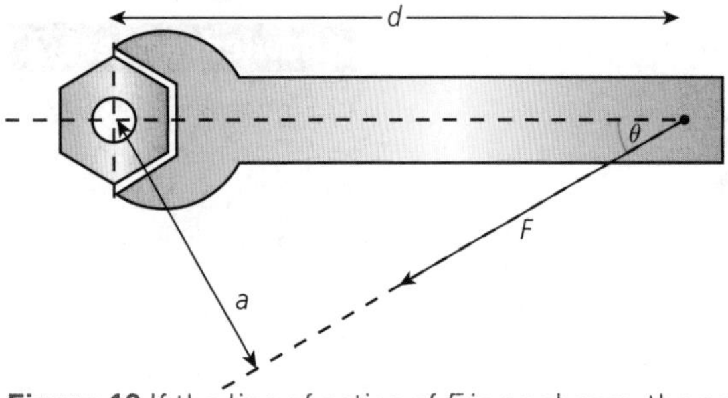

Figure 10 If the line of action of F is as shown, the perpendicular distance to the line of action is $a = d \sin \theta$

In Figure 10, the moment of force, F, about the centre of the nut is given by:

$$F \times a = F \times d \sin \theta$$

This is the same as:

$$d \times F \sin \theta$$

where $F \sin \theta$ is the component of the force F at right angles to the spanner.

Couple

Often there are two equal and opposite coplanar (parallel) forces applied to turn something. An example of this is shown in Figure 11. These forces are known as a couple. Each force in the couple provides a moment. The moment of this couple is defined as:

force × perpendicular distance between the lines of action of the forces

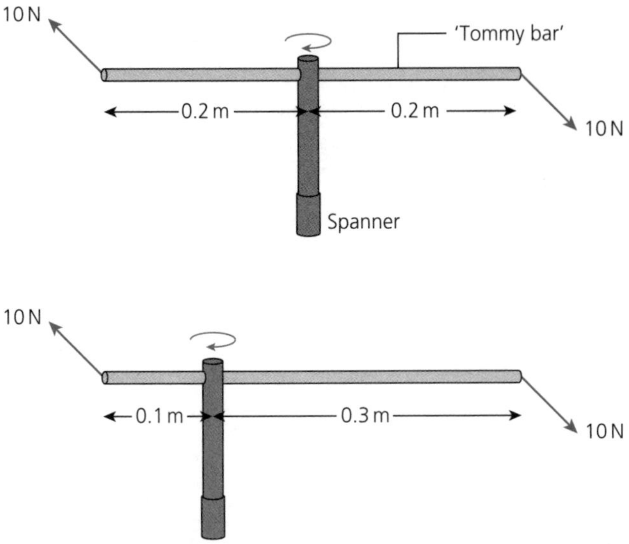

Figure 11 A couple acts on a spanner as shown. The moment of the couple in both cases is 10 × 0.4 = 4 N m

Principle of moments

Moments of forces will try to turn a body either clockwise or anticlockwise, so are termed clockwise or anticlockwise moments.

When a body is in equilibrium, the sum of the clockwise moments about any point is equal to the sum of the anticlockwise moments about that same point. This is known as the principle of moments.

Exam tip

Always distinguish between the clockwise and anticlockwise moments in your calculations.

Worked example

Figure 12 shows a car on a bridge. The car is 10 m from point B. The roadway has a weight of 350 kN and the car has a weight of 10 kN.

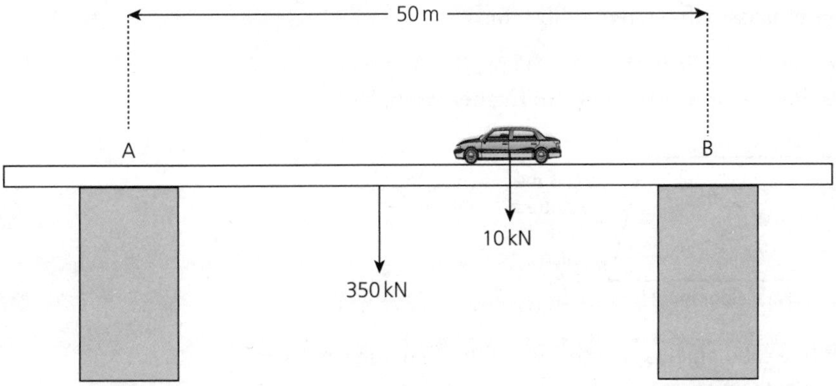

Figure 12

Calculate the forces, F_A and F_B, exerted by the supports on the bridge at point A and point B.

→

Answer

The bridge with the car on it is in equilibrium. Taking moments about point B:

clockwise moment = $F_A \times 50$

anticlockwise moments = $(10 \times 10) + (350 \times 25) = 8850\,\text{kN m}$

clockwise moments = anticlockwise moments

$F_A \times 50 = 8850\,\text{kN m}$

$F_A = 177\,\text{kN}$

Since total upward force must equal total downward force:

$F_A + F_B = 350 + 10 = 360\,\text{kN}$

$F_B = 183\,\text{kN}$

Check by taking moments about point A:

clockwise moments = $(350 \times 25) + (10 \times 40) = 9150\,\text{kN m}$

anticlockwise moment = $F_B \times 50$

clockwise moments = anticlockwise moments

$F_B \times 50 = 9150\,\text{kN m}$

$F_B = 183\,\text{kN}$

Knowledge check 4

If the car in Figure 12 moves to be 30 m from point B, calculate the forces, F_A and F_B, exerted by the supports on the bridge at point A and point B.

Centre of mass

The centre of mass of an object is the single point at which we can assume the mass is acting for the purposes of calculations.

An object supported at its centre of mass will be in equilibrium.

The centre of mass of a regular solid object is at its centre. Thus, the centre of mass of a sphere is at the centre of the sphere. Figure 13 shows two further examples.

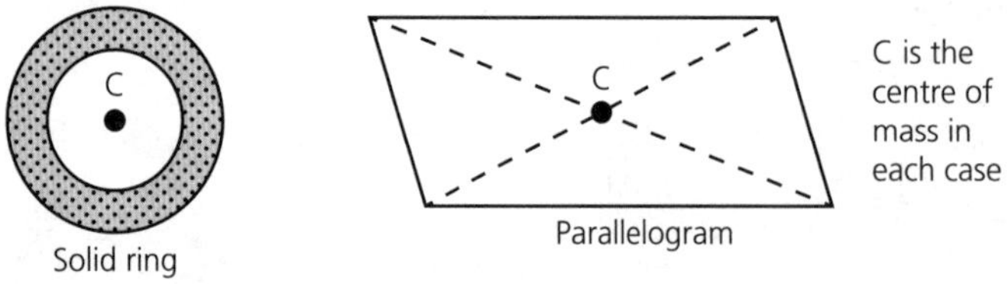

Figure 13 The centre of mass of two solid objects. In the case of the ring, the centre of mass is in the space in the middle of the ring

Worked example

Figure 14 shows a 1 m ruler balanced 20 cm from one end by a force of 1.2 N acting downwards on the end.

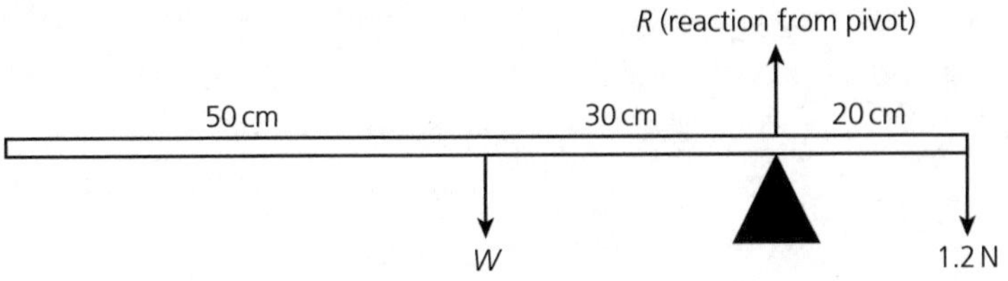

Figure 14

Calculate the weight of the ruler.

Answer

The ruler has a uniform shape and density, so the centre of mass is in the centre of the ruler, 50 cm from one end.

clockwise moment = $1.2 \times 0.2 = 0.24$ N m

anticlockwise moment = $W \times 0.30$

clockwise moments = anticlockwise moments

$$W = \frac{0.24}{0.34} = 0.80\,\text{N}$$

Knowledge check 5

What happens to the centre of mass of a spherical ball as it rolls along a flat horizontal surface?

Summary

After studying this topic you should:

- know that the moment of a force is defined as the force × the perpendicular distance from the point to the line of action of the force
- know that for an object in equilibrium the clockwise moments about any point are equal to the anticlockwise moments about that point
- be able to calculate the clockwise moments and anticlockwise moments about any point
- know that the moment of a couple is the force × the perpendicular distance between the lines of action of the forces
- be able to identify the centre of mass of any uniform regular solid

Motion along a straight line

Displacement, speed, velocity and acceleration

Displacement is a vector quantity and is the distance in a given direction.

If an object is moving at a steady speed in a given direction, it has a constant velocity. Velocity is also a vector quantity.

A graph of displacement (s) against time (t) for an object moving at a constant velocity might look like Figure 15.

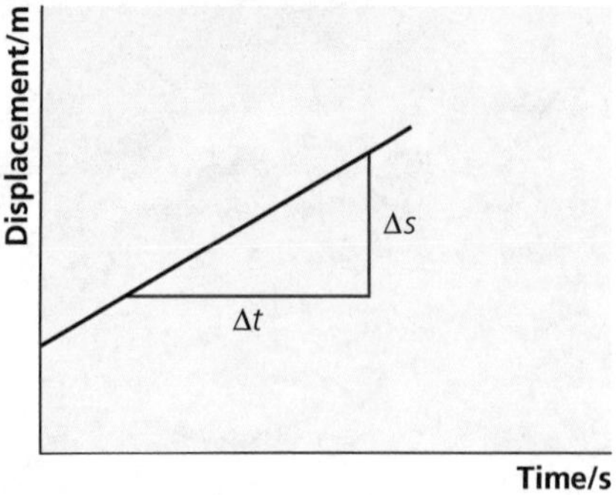

Figure 15 A graph showing an object moving at a constant speed in a given direction

The gradient of a displacement–time graph gives the velocity, v, of the object:

$$v = \frac{\Delta s}{\Delta t}$$

A more useful graph is one of velocity against time, as shown in Figure 16.

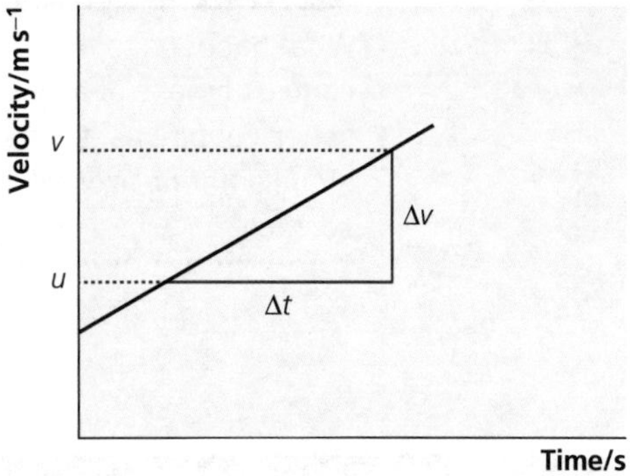

Figure 16 In this case, the object's velocity is not constant but is increasing uniformly. This is constant acceleration

Acceleration, a, is the change of velocity divided by the time taken for the change and is given by the gradient of a velocity–time graph:

$$a = \frac{\Delta v}{\Delta t}$$

In this case:

$$\Delta v = v - u$$

Therefore, for objects moving with constant acceleration:

$$a = \frac{v - u}{\Delta t}$$

$$\Rightarrow v = u + a\Delta t$$

This is one of the five equations of motion.

Displacement can be found from a velocity–time graph, as shown in Figure 17.

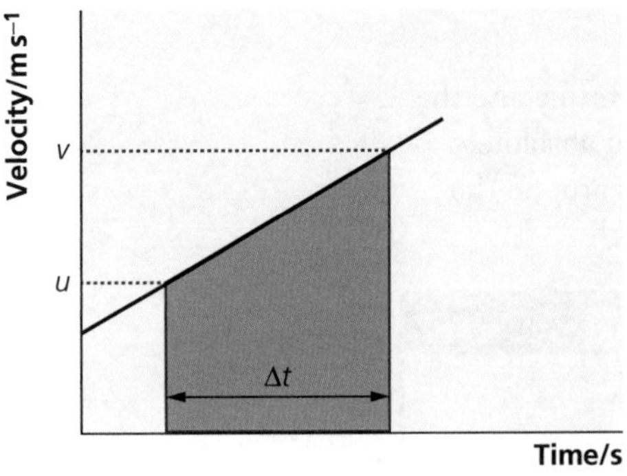

Figure 17 The area under a velocity–time graph is the displacement. In this case, the displacement in the time Δt is shown by the shaded area

Displacement, s, is the average velocity multiplied by the time taken:

$$s = \frac{v+u}{2} \times \Delta t$$

This is another of the five equations of motion.

Knowledge check 6

In Figure 17, u is $8.0\,\mathrm{m\,s^{-1}}$ at $t = 9.0\,\mathrm{s}$ and v is $15\,\mathrm{m\,s^{-1}}$ at $t = 12\,\mathrm{s}$. Calculate the distance travelled between 9.0 s and 12 s.

Equations of motion

By combining the above two equations of motion in different ways, we can derive all five equations of motion for constant acceleration. In practice, we usually use t rather than the more correct Δt to indicate a time interval.

$$s = \frac{v+u}{2} \times t$$

$$s = ut + \frac{1}{2}at^2$$

$$v = u + at$$

$$v^2 = u^2 + 2as$$

$$a = \frac{v-u}{t}$$

With these five equations, most problems involving uniform motion can be solved.

Worked example

A car travelling at $10\,\mathrm{m\,s^{-1}}$ accelerates uniformly at $2\,\mathrm{m\,s^{-2}}$ for 10 s. Calculate the final velocity and the displacement in this time.

Answer

To find the final velocity use:

$$v = u + at$$

$$v = 10 + (2 \times 10) = 30\,\mathrm{m\,s^{-1}}$$

To find the displacement use:

$$s = ut + \frac{1}{2}at^2$$

$$s = (10 \times 10) + \left(\frac{1}{2} \times 2 \times 10^2\right) = 200\,\mathrm{m}$$

Exam tip

When you start a question, write down which quantities you know and which ones you need to find out so that you can check which of the equations of motion is the most suitable.

Acceleration due to gravity

The acceleration due to gravity on Earth, g, has been measured very carefully and the accepted value for the surface of the Earth is 9.81 m s^{-2}. The value is not absolutely constant though because there are small differences for different places around the planet. In many calculations, an approximation of 10 m s^{-2} is good enough.

Required practical 3

Determination of g by a freefall method

The value of g can be measured in the laboratory by timing a falling object. A possible arrangement is shown in Figure 18 but there are many variations of this apparatus, including the use of data-loggers with light gates. You should know how to carry out this experiment using any suitable method.

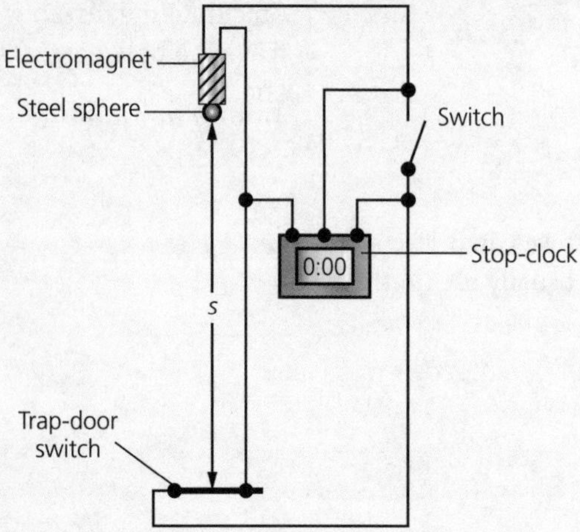

Figure 18 Apparatus for measuring g

The steel sphere is released from the electromagnet and is allowed to fall freely. As it is released, the stop-clock starts and when the sphere hits the trap-door switch the stop-clock stops. The distance between the bottom of the sphere (when attached to the electromagnet) and the trap-door switch is the distance fallen, s, in the measured time, t.

We can use this equation of motion to find a:

$$s = ut + \frac{1}{2}at^2$$

The initial velocity, u, is zero and a is equal to g, so the equation simplifies to:

$$s = \frac{1}{2}gt^2$$

Rearranged:

$$g = \frac{2s}{t^2}$$

A precise value of g could be found by taking many values of t for the same s. However, it is better to take values of t for different values of s and then plot a graph of displacement against time^2, which will have a gradient of $g/2$.

In an experiment to find g, the data in Table 1 are obtained.

Displacement/m	0.00	0.20	0.40	0.60	0.80	1.00	1.20	1.40	1.60
Time/s	0.00	0.20	0.29	0.35	0.40	0.45	0.49	0.53	0.57

Table 1

Use these data to plot a graph of displacement against time^2 and then measure the gradient of your graph. From the gradient of your graph, calculate the value of g.

A similar graph might look like Figure 19. In this case, the gradient is 4.9 m s^{-2} which gives a value of g of 9.8 m s^{-2}.

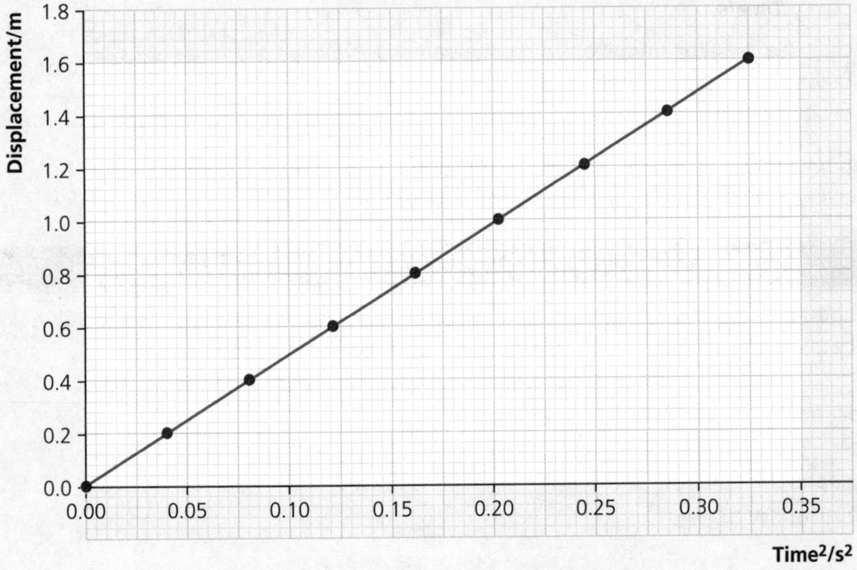

Figure 19 Graph of displacement against time^2 for a falling sphere

You should consider the uncertainty in the measurement of the displacement and time. If displacement is measured with a metre rule, the uncertainty is ±1 mm. The uncertainty in time will be ±0.005 s.

Which variables should be controlled? The mass and diameter of the steel sphere should not be changed otherwise the air resistance may change.

Exam tip

You should be able to describe how to measure g by a freefall method and how to reduce the uncertainties in your measurements.

Non-uniform acceleration

Unlike a falling sphere, the acceleration of an object may not be uniform which means that the velocity may not change uniformly. For example, a graph of velocity against time for a space rocket taking off might look like Figure 20.

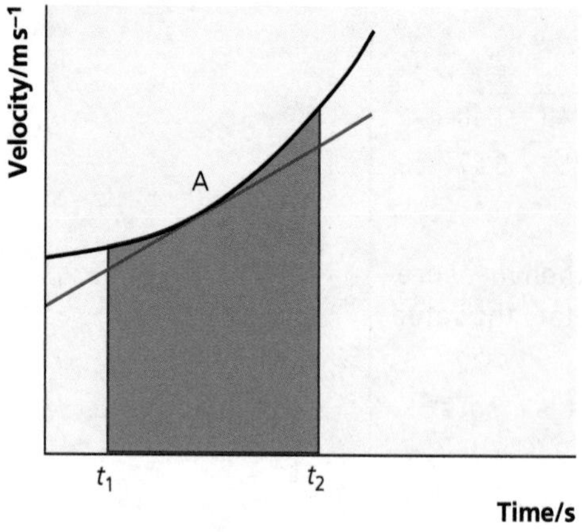

Figure 20 The acceleration of a rocket will not be uniform, even if the engine thrust is constant, because its mass changes during the journey and, over the distance travelled, g will also change

The acceleration of the rocket at any point, such as A, is given by the gradient of the graph. The displacement between times t_1 and t_2 is given by the shaded area.

Knowledge check 7

Sketch the velocity–time graph and the displacement–time graph for a ball dropped from a height of 1.0 m and which bounces to a height of 0.80 m. Take the acceleration due to gravity as 9.8 m s^{-2}.

Summary

After studying this topic you should:

- be able to calculate velocity from a displacement–time graph
- be able to calculate acceleration from a velocity–time graph
- be able to sketch motion graphs for objects moving with uniform and non-uniform acceleration
- be able to use the equations of motion to solve problems with uniform acceleration
- know how to measure g using laboratory apparatus

Projectile motion

The equations of motion can be applied to the motion of a projectile.

In the simple case, an object is projected horizontally at a velocity, v. The motion of the object is described by treating the horizontal motion and the vertical motion separately. The object will accelerate downwards because of gravity acting on it. Horizontally, it will continue to travel at a constant velocity because there is no horizontal force acting on it apart from air resistance, which we will ignore at present.

The motion of the object follows a parabolic path, as shown in Figure 21. In this example, the object was thrown horizontally at a velocity of 10 m s^{-1} from a height of 1.8 m.

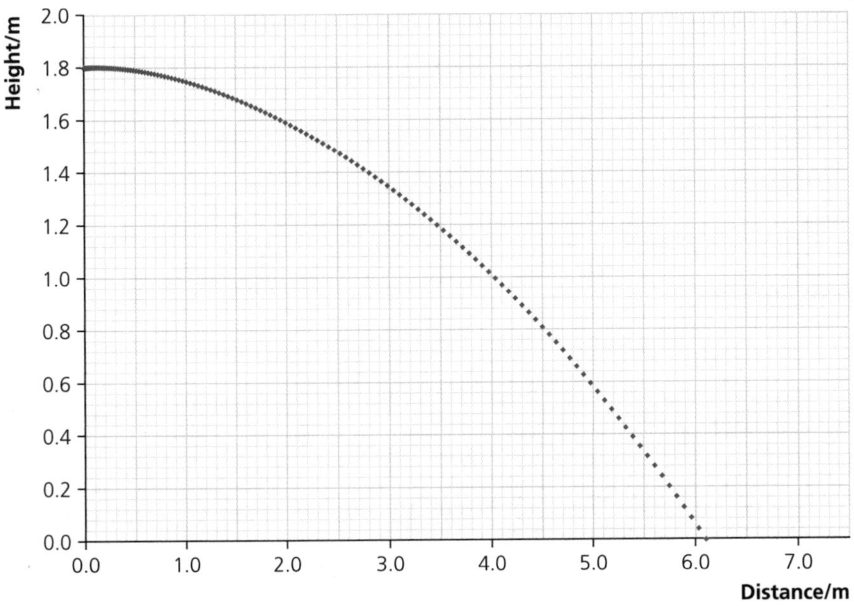

Figure 21 An object thrown horizontally follows a parabolic path

Worked example

For the object shown in Figure 21, calculate the time taken for it to hit the ground and show that it will hit the ground about 6 m from where it was thrown.

Answer

For the vertical motion, to calculate the time, t, for the object to hit the ground use:

$$s = ut + \frac{1}{2}at^2$$

Rearranging and substituting $s = 1.8\,\text{m}$, $a = 9.8\,\text{m}\,\text{s}^{-2}$ and $u = 0\,\text{m}\,\text{s}^{-1}$:

$$t^2 = \frac{2 \times 1.8}{9.8} = 0.37\,\text{s}$$

$$\Rightarrow t = 0.61\,\text{s}$$

For the horizontal motion, moving at $10\,\text{m}\,\text{s}^{-1}$ for 0.61 s, the object will travel 6.1 m.

Exam tip

Remember that for projectile motion, the horizontal and vertical motion can be treated separately.

It does not matter what the horizontal velocity is, the object will still hit the ground after the same amount of time, assuming that we ignore air resistance.

The object does not have to be thrown horizontally. If it is thrown upwards, it still follows a parabolic path, as shown in Figure 22.

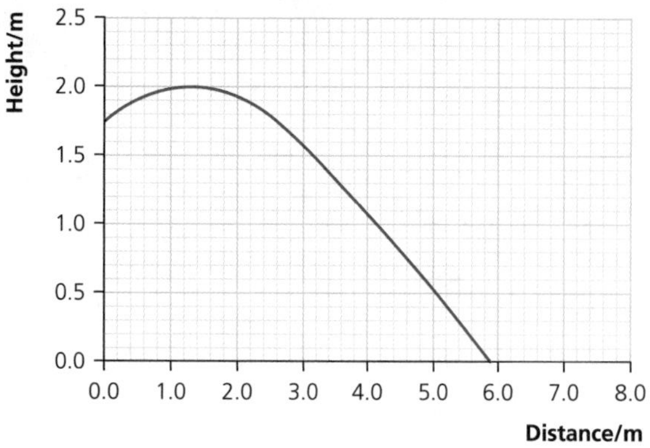

Figure 22 The object is now thrown upwards from a height of 1.8 m with a vertical component of 2.0 m s^{-1}and a horizontal component of 7.0 m s^{-1}

The calculation is similar to the one for Figure 21, but this time u is $-2.0\,\text{m s}^{-1}$. The negative sign indicates that the velocity is in the opposite direction to the acceleration.

To calculate t use:

$$s = ut + \frac{1}{2}at^2$$

$$1.8 = (-2.0 \times t) + \left(\frac{1}{2} \times 9.8 \times t^2\right)$$

$$\Rightarrow 4.9t^2 - 2.0t - 1.8 = 0$$

This can be solved for t using the formula for the solution of a quadratic equation. This gives $t = 0.84$ s, so it takes 0.84 s for the object to reach the ground. Using this, the distance travelled horizontally can then be calculated:

$$0.84 \times 7.0 = 5.9\,\text{m}$$

Knowledge check 8

A ball is thrown upwards with a velocity of 3.0 m s^{-1} from a height of 2.0 m. Calculate the time it takes to reach the ground assuming no air resistance.

Air resistance

In real situations of motion through air, there will be some air resistance (drag). Air resistance will modify the path of a projectile, depending on the velocity of the object and its shape. In general, air resistance depends on the square of the velocity of the object through the air. It also depends on the density of the air, the surface of the object, and the size and shape of the object.

In Figure 23, the black parabola shows an object thrown upwards without any air resistance. The two other parabolas show objects thrown upwards with the same velocity but with differing air resistance. The object shown by the blue parabola experiences less air resistance than the object shown by the green parabola.

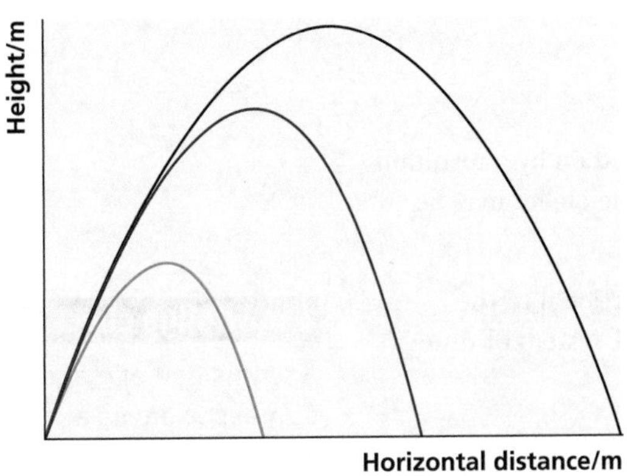

Figure 23 Three objects thrown upwards, experiencing differing amounts of air resistance

Most vehicles are designed to be as aerodynamic as possible. Large lorries often have spoilers on top of the cab to improve the air flow over the lorry and so reduce the drag. This makes a significant difference to the fuel efficiency of a lorry. Racing cars are also designed to reduce the air resistance as much as possible so as to increase their maximum speed.

A spinning object, or an object with different surfaces on the top and bottom (such as a cricket ball that the bowler has polished on one side), can generate different amounts of lift and drag so that the parabolic path of a projectile can be modified by careful design. For example, the path of a cricket ball or a golf ball can be modified by the spin applied to the ball when it is projected.

Because of the air resistance experienced by a falling object, it will not accelerate at a uniform rate indefinitely. As the velocity increases, so does the air resistance and eventually this will become equal to the weight of the object and the resultant force will become zero. At this point, the downward velocity will remain constant and the object is said to be falling at its terminal speed. This terminal speed will depend significantly on the cross-sectional area of the object. For example, a skydiver wanting to reduce her terminal speed will fall in a horizontal position with arms outstretched. Some skydivers have fabric 'wings' between their arms and the body of their skydiving suit to help reduce their terminal speed.

Summary

After studying this topic you should:

- know that horizontal and vertical motion for a projectile can be treated separately
- be able to apply the equations of motion to horizontal and vertical motion
- know that real projectiles experience drag and that in air this drag is called air resistance
- know that when the air resistance acting on a falling object is equal to its weight it will continue to fall at its terminal speed

Newton's laws of motion

Newton's three laws of motion are:

Law 1: an object will continue with a constant velocity unless acted on by a resultant force. The constant velocity may be any value, including zero, so the object may be at rest.

Law 2: the rate of change of velocity of an object is directly proportional to the resultant force and inversely proportional to the mass. Using the SI system of units, the constant of proportionality is 1, so this law is often quoted as:

$$a = \frac{F}{m} \quad \text{or} \quad F = ma$$

where a is the rate of change of velocity, or acceleration, F is the resultant force on the object and m is the mass of the object.

The unit of acceleration is $m\,s^{-2}$ and the unit of force is N. Therefore, 1 N is equivalent to $1\,kg\,m\,s^{-2}$.

Law 3: if body A exerts a force on body B, then body B will exert an equal and opposite force of the same type on body A.

Newton's third law often causes confusion. The pairs of forces described in this law need to be understood fully.

In Figure 24(a), there are two pairs of forces. The diver is being pulled downwards towards the Earth by gravity. The equal and opposite force to this force, of the same type and size, is the Earth being pulled upwards towards the diver. The Earth does not obviously move because its mass is extremely large so, by Newton's second law, the acceleration of the Earth is very small and you will not be able to measure its movement.

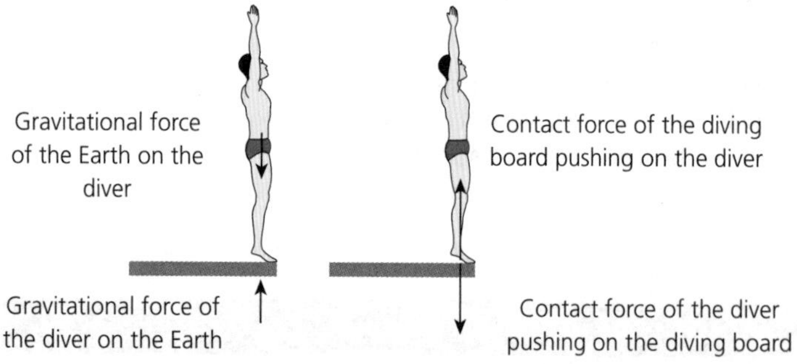

Figure 24(a) Forces acting on a diver and diving board

The second pair of forces is the contact forces. The diver is pushing down on the diving board with a force equal to his weight. The diving board is pushing up on the diver with an equal and opposite force.

Figure 24(b) shows the forces acting on the diver only. There are two forces, the diver's weight downwards and the diving board pushing upwards. These two forces are equal and opposite, so the resultant force is zero and the diver has no acceleration. However, they are not a pair of forces as defined by Newton's third law.

Knowledge check 9

A tennis ball of mass 60 g experiences a force of 300 N during a serve. Calculate the acceleration of the ball during the impact with the tennis racquet.

Exam tip

Make sure you can quote Newton's three laws of motion.

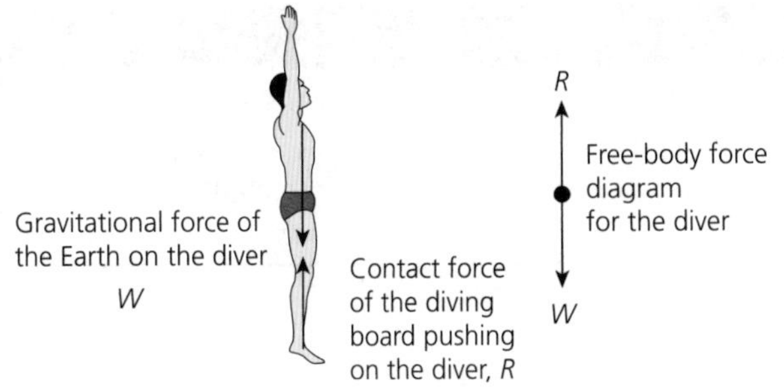

Figure 24(b) Forces acting on the diver only

In Figure 24(c), the diver is falling towards the water. There is still a pair of gravitational forces acting, but now there is no pair of contact forces.

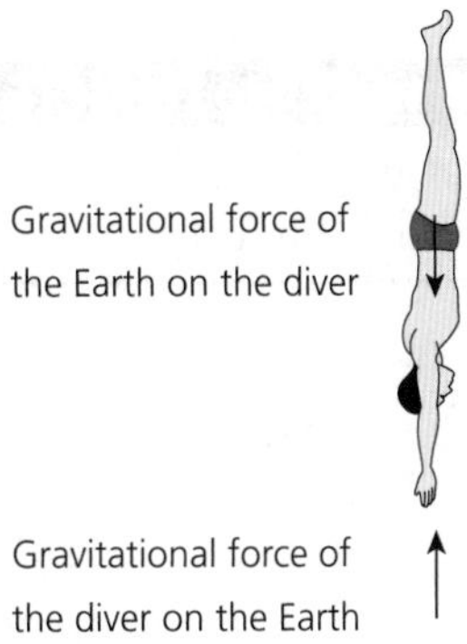

Figure 24(c) Forces acting as the diver falls towards the water

Looking at the forces on the diver, there is only his weight downwards which means that there is a resultant force, $m \times g$, and by Newton's second law this causes an acceleration downwards of:

$$a = \frac{mg}{m} = g$$

Exam tip

Practise drawing free-body force diagrams for different objects and situations.

Knowledge check 10

Figure 25 shows a car towing a caravan that has a mass of 500 kg. The force of the car on the caravan is 400 N and the trailer experiences a frictional force of 100 N.

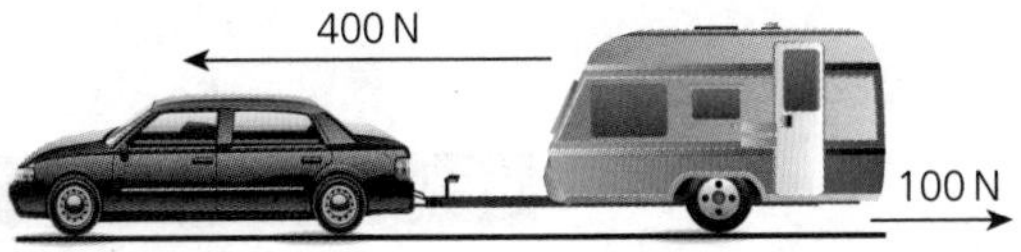

Figure 25

a As described by Newton's third law, list the four pairs of forces acting on the caravan.

b Calculate the acceleration of the caravan.

Summary

After studying this topic you should:

- be able to write down Newton's three laws of motion
- be able to calculate force, mass or acceleration from $F = ma$
- be able to identify pairs of forces as described by Newton's third law
- be able to draw free-body force diagrams

Momentum

Momentum and impulse

The quantity called momentum is defined as:

momentum = mass × velocity

As velocity is a vector quantity, mass × velocity is also a vector quantity.

The unit of mass is kg and the unit of velocity is m s^{-1}. Therefore, the unit of momentum is kg m s^{-1} or N s.

Momentum is a conserved quantity so, in any collision or explosion, the quantity remains constant. This is as true of a collision between galaxies as it is for collisions of fundamental particles. Momentum is conserved in all directions, so the components of momentum in any given direction must also be conserved.

The conservation of momentum follows from Newton's laws. As already seen, Newton's second law can be stated as:

force = mass × acceleration

$$\Rightarrow \text{force} = \text{mass} \times \frac{\Delta v}{\Delta t}$$

This can be rewritten as:

$$\text{force} = \frac{\Delta mv}{\Delta t}$$

In words, this states that force equals the rate of change of momentum.

This can be further rewritten as:

$$F \times \Delta t = \Delta mv$$

The quantity $F \times \Delta t$ is called the **impulse** and is equal to the change of momentum as long as the force, F, is constant.

Newton's third law states that in any collision, the force of body A on body B is equal and opposite to the force of body B on body A, and the time of contact must be the same for both bodies. Therefore, the change of momentum of body A must be equal and opposite to the change of momentum of body B. Thus, momentum is always conserved.

Knowledge check 11

Show that N s is equivalent to kg m s^{-1}.

Impulse is the product of force and time for which the force acts. Impulse is equal to the change of momentum. The unit of impulse is N s or kg m s^{-1}.

Knowledge check 12

What is the momentum of a trolley of mass 2 kg moving at a velocity of $0.5\,\text{m s}^{-1}$?

Worked example

Figure 26 shows a trolley of mass 1.0 kg moving at a velocity of $2.0\,m\,s^{-1}$. It collides with a stationary trolley of mass 0.50 kg and sticks to it.

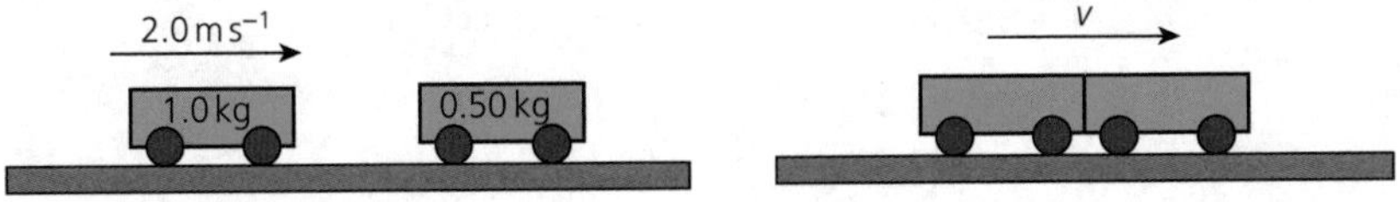

Figure 26

Calculate the velocity of the two trolleys after the collision.

Answer

The momentum before the collision was:

$$(m_1 \times u_1) + (m_2 \times u_2) = (1.0 \times 2.0) + (0.50 \times 0.0) = 2.0\,kg\,m\,s^{-1}$$

This must equal the momentum after the collision:

$$(1.0 + 0.50) \times v = 2.0\,kg\,m\,s^{-1}$$

$$v = 1.3\,m\,s^{-1}$$

Two objects that collide may have been travelling in opposite directions before the collision. Momentum is still conserved.

Worked example

Calculate the velocity of the left-hand ball in Figure 27 after the collision. After the collision, the ball on the right recoils at $3.4\,m\,s^{-1}$.

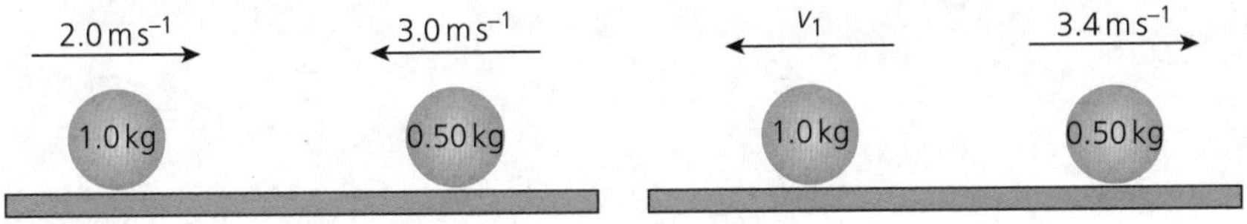

Figure 27

Answer

The momentum before the collision was:

$$(m_1 \times u_1) + (m_2 \times u_2) = (1.0 \times 2.0) + (0.50 \times -3.0) = 0.5\,kg\,m\,s^{-1}$$

As momentum before the collision must equal momentum after the collision:

$$(m_1 \times v_1) + (m_2 \times v_2) = (1.0 \times v_1) + (0.50 \times 3.4) = 0.50\,kg\,m\,s^{-1}$$

$v_1 = -1.2\,m\,s^{-1}$ (the negative sign shows it is moving to the left)

Force and time in a collision

A graph of force against time for constant force in a collision would look like Figure 28.

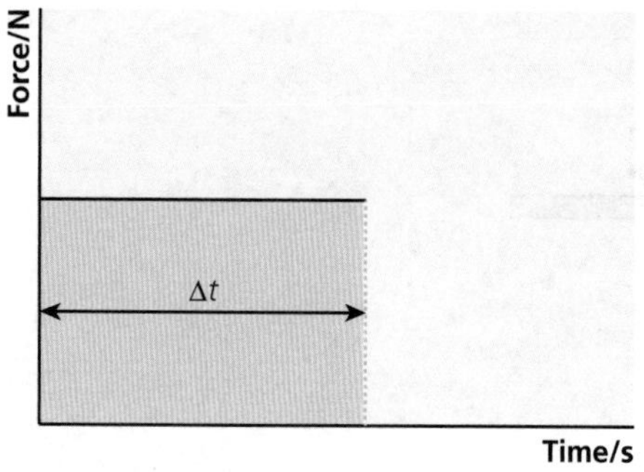

Figure 28 The force between two objects in a collision

The area under the graph is:

$F \times \Delta t$ = impulse = change of momentum

Even if the force in a collision is not constant, the area under the force–time graph still gives the change of momentum.

In Figure 29, the change of momentum of the tennis ball is given by the area under the force–time graph. By counting the squares on the graph, you can see that the change of momentum is about 4.0 N s.

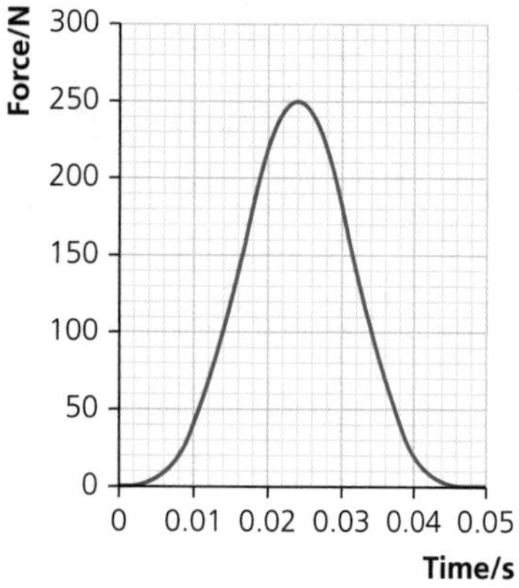

Figure 29 The force applied to a tennis ball when it is hit. The mass of the ball is 60 g

For the tennis ball:

$m \times \Delta v = 4.0\,\text{N s}$

Therefore:

$\Delta v = 67\,\text{m s}^{-1}$

The value of Δv is the final velocity minus the initial velocity. Therefore, if the ball was travelling towards the racquet at $-30\,\text{m s}^{-1}$, it must leave the racquet at $+37\,\text{m s}^{-1}$, indicating it is now travelling in the opposite direction.

Knowledge check 13

A car of mass 900 kg travelling at $13\,\text{m s}^{-1}$ is brought to rest in 3.0 s by hitting a wall.

a Calculate the impulse applied to the car.

b Calculate the average force exerted on the car by the wall.

Exam tip

Remember that the change in any quantity is always the final value minus the initial value.

The idea of impulse is used in the design of many safety features, for example in road vehicles. Cars are designed with crumple zones so that in the event of a collision, the time over which the change of momentum occurs is extended, thus reducing the average force. This helps to reduce injury to any occupants of the car and can also help to reduce injury should the collision be with a person or animal.

Seat belts are designed to stretch so that the time taken to change the momentum of the driver or passenger is extended. This reduces the maximum force on the person, which helps to reduce injury. Another safety feature in road vehicles is air bags. These inflate rapidly in a collision so that the driver or passenger is slowed down by the air bag, rather than by hitting the dashboard, steering wheel or windscreen. This further helps to reduce injury.

In clothing design, trainers for running on roads are designed to be cushioned so that the force on the foot and leg joints is reduced by increasing the time taken to change the momentum of the foot and leg.

In everyday life, when we jump we tend to naturally bend our knees on landing in order to increase the time over which our momentum is changed, thus reducing the maximum force exerted on our legs.

Elastic and inelastic collisions and explosions

In any collision or explosion, momentum is always conserved. However, kinetic energy is not usually conserved. A collision in which kinetic energy is conserved is called an **elastic collision** and one in which kinetic energy is not conserved is an **inelastic collision**. Generally only collisions when there is no contact, for example when two magnets interact, can be elastic. Collisions between subatomic particles can also be regarded as elastic.

An **elastic collision** is one in which kinetic energy is conserved. An **inelastic collision** is one in which kinetic energy is not conserved. Most collisions are inelastic.

Worked example

Two trolleys of mass 1.0 kg and 0.8 kg are pushed together with a spring between them, as shown in Figure 30. The trolleys are at rest when the spring is released and they then fly apart ('explode'). The 1.0 kg trolley moves away at a velocity of 2.0 m s^{-1}.

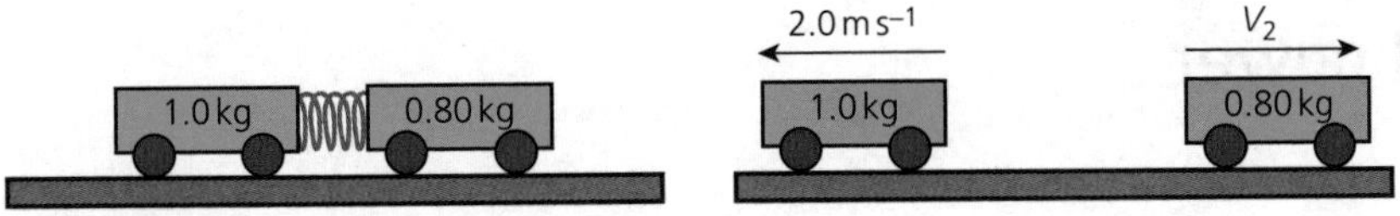

Figure 30

a Calculate the velocity of the 0.80 kg trolley.

b Calculate the total kinetic energy before and after the 'explosion'.

c Explain where the kinetic energy came from.

→

Answers

a The momentum before the explosion is zero as the trolleys are stationary. By conservation of momentum, the total momentum after the explosion must also be zero:

$(m_1 \times v_1) + (m_2 \times v_2) = 0$

$(1.0 \times 2.0) + (0.80 \times v_2) = 0$

$2.0\,\text{kg}\,\text{m}\,\text{s}^{-1} = -0.80 v_2$

$v_2 = -2.5\,\text{m}\,\text{s}^{-1}$ (the negative sign indicates that the 0.80 kg trolley is moving in the opposite direction to the 1.0 kg trolley)

b The total kinetic energy before the explosion is zero as the trolleys are not moving. After the collision:

total kinetic energy $= (\frac{1}{2} \times m_1 \times v_1{}^2) + (\frac{1}{2} \times m_2 \times v_2{}^2)$

total kinetic energy $= (\frac{1}{2} \times 1.0 \times 2.0^2) + (\frac{1}{2} \times 0.80 \times 2.5^2) = 4.5\,\text{J}$

c The kinetic energy came from the strain energy stored in the compressed spring.

Summary

After studying this topic you should:

- be able to calculate the momentum of a moving object
- be able to calculate the change of momentum in a collision or explosion
- be able to use your value of change of momentum to calculate the velocity of one object after the collision or explosion
- be able to calculate impulse
- be able to apply the idea of impulse to safety features in road vehicles
- know the difference between an elastic and inelastic collision or explosion

Work, energy and power

Work and energy

Work, energy and power are connected. When **work** is done on an object, the object gains energy. A body can also transfer energy by doing work. Power is the rate at which work is done.

Work is defined as:

$$\Delta W = F \times \Delta x$$

Where x is the distance moved in the direction of the force.

When the point at which a 1 N force is applied moves through 1 m in the direction of the force, 1 J of work is done. 1 joule is equal to 1 N m.

Work is defined as the force multiplied by the distance moved in the direction of the applied force. When the force is measured in N and the distance in m, the unit of work is the joule, J.

Worked example

A supermarket trolley is pushed for 5 m in a straight line with a force of 25 N. Calculate the work done.

Answer

work done = $F \times \Delta x = 25 \times 5 = 125\,\text{N m} = 125\,\text{J}$

When something is lifted, the force needed to support it is equal to its weight.

weight = $m \times g$

When an object of mass m is lifted through a distance, Δh:

work done = $mg\Delta h$

This will be the amount of gravitational potential energy gained by the object.

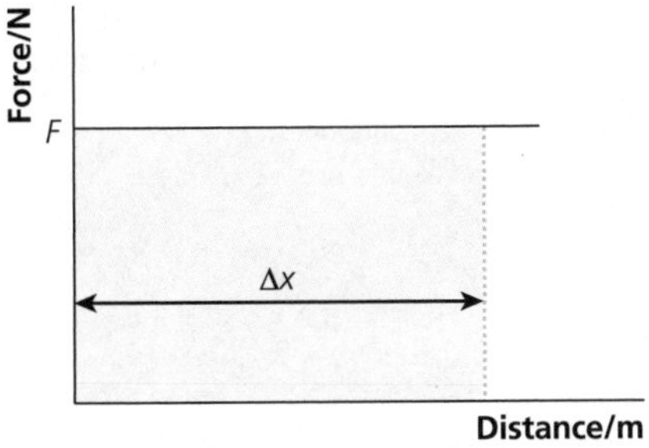

Figure 31 Graph showing a constant force moving through a distance, x

Figure 31 shows a constant force, F, being applied over a distance, x. The work done when the force is moved a distance Δx in the direction of the force is given by $F\Delta x$. It can be seen that this is the shaded area under the graph. Therefore:

work done = area under a force–distance graph

This is true even when the force is not constant, as in the case of a spring being stretched.

In Figure 32, a spring is being stretched. The force is proportional to the extension, Δl.

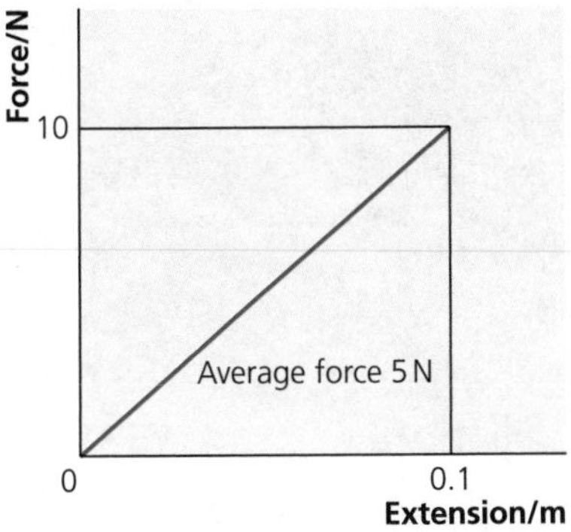

Figure 32 A spring that obeys Hooke's law being stretched

Exam tip

If you are counting squares under a graph, it generally works as a good estimate to count any that are more than half as one square and not to count any that are less than half a square.

The work done in stretching the spring is given by the area under the graph. In this case:

$$\text{work done} = \frac{1}{2}F\Delta l = \frac{1}{2} \times 10 \times 0.1 = 0.5\,\text{J}$$

The value 0.5 J is also the value for the energy stored in the spring as strain energy.

The force is not always in the same direction as the distance moved by an object. In Figure 33, a sleigh is being pulled through the snow by a force acting at an angle θ to the horizontal.

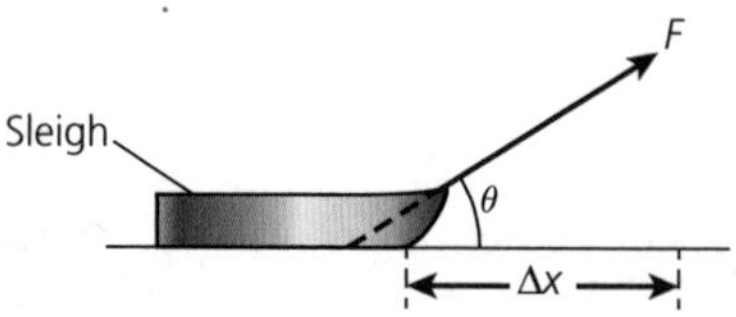

Figure 33 A sleigh being pulled along at an angle θ to the horizontal

In this case, the component of the force in the direction of motion is $F\cos\theta$. Therefore, the work done is:

$$F\cos\theta \times \Delta x = F\Delta x\cos\theta$$

Power

Power is the rate at which work is done. It is defined as:

$$\text{power} = \frac{\Delta W}{\Delta t} = \frac{\Delta E}{\Delta t}$$

The unit of work is J and the unit of time is s. Therefore, the unit of power is J s^{-1}. One joule per second is equal to 1 W (watt).

Power is the rate at which work is done or the rate of transfer of energy.

Worked example

A student lifts a box of mass 20 kg a distance of 3.0 m vertically in 8.0 s. Calculate the average power expended by the student.

Answer

$$\text{work done} = mg\Delta h = 20 \times 9.8 \times 3.0 = 588\,\text{J}$$

$$\text{power} = \frac{\Delta W}{\Delta t} = \frac{588}{8.0} = 74\,\text{W}$$

The power of an object moving at a constant speed with a constant resistive force can be found using the force and speed:

$$\text{power} = \frac{\Delta W}{\Delta t} = \frac{F \times \Delta x}{\Delta t}$$

Substituting:

$$\frac{\Delta x}{\Delta t} = v$$

Therefore:

$$\text{power} = F \times v$$

Worked example

A train is travelling at $35\,\text{m s}^{-1}$ and the resistive force is 20 kN. Calculate the power of the electric motors.

Answer

$$\text{power} = 20 \times 10^3 \times 35 = 7.0 \times 10^5\,\text{W} = 700\,\text{kW}$$

Efficiency

In almost every situation where work is done or energy is transferred, some of the energy is not transferred to the required output work. For example, not all the energy stored in the fuel for a car is transferred to kinetic energy. A certain amount is lost as heat to the surroundings.

The efficiency of a system, usually expressed as a percentage, is given by:

$$\text{efficiency} = \frac{\text{useful energy output}}{\text{energy input}} \times 100\% = \frac{\text{useful power output}}{\text{power input}} \times 100\%$$

Exam tip

Efficiency can be calculated using energy or power.

Worked example

A lift when fully laden has a total mass of 1000 kg. It is able to go up five floors, a distance of 15 m, in 30 s. While doing so, the electric motor draws a power of 6.0 kW from the electricity supply. Calculate the efficiency of the system.

Answer

The work done in lifting 1000 kg through 15 m is:

$$mg\Delta h = 1000 \times 9.8 \times 15 = 1.47 \times 10^5\,\text{J} = 147\,\text{kJ}$$

$$\text{power} = \frac{\Delta W}{\Delta t} = \frac{147 \times 10^3}{30} = 4.9 \times 10^3\,\text{W}$$

$$\text{efficiency} = \frac{\text{useful power output}}{\text{power input}} \times 100\%$$

$$= \frac{4.9 \times 10^3}{6.0 \times 10^3} \times 100\% = 82\%$$

Knowledge check 14

Most internal combustion engines are between 30% and 40% efficient. Why is the efficiency so low?

Summary

After studying this topic you should:

- be able to calculate work done
- understand the idea of power and be able to calculate power
- be able to calculate the efficiency of a process involving energy transfer

Conservation of energy

Energy cannot be created or destroyed. It is converted into other forms when work is done. The conservation of energy is one of the fundamental principles of physics. One area in which it can be applied is when calculating work done in mechanical situations, such as moving or falling objects.

Gravitational potential energy

Gravitational potential energy is the ability of a body to do work because of its position in a gravitational field. We usually measure the *change* in gravitational potential energy because that is the more useful quantity.

We have already seen that when an object of mass m is lifted through a distance, Δh, the work done is:

$$\Delta W = mg\Delta h$$

This is the amount of gravitational potential energy, ΔE_p, gained by the object. Therefore, we can say:

$$\Delta E_p = mg\Delta h$$

The value of ΔE_p is measured in joules provided that m is in kg, g is in $N\,kg^{-1}$ and Δh is in m.

Knowledge check 15

A box of mass 5.0 kg is lifted from the ground onto a shelf at a height of 2.0 m. Calculate the gain in gravitational potential energy of the box.

Kinetic energy

A moving object will either require work to be done on it to increase its speed or it will have to do work in order to decrease its speed. When work is done, energy is transferred from one form to another.

A moving object therefore has energy associated with its motion. This is called kinetic energy, E_k, and is defined as:

$$E_k = \frac{1}{2}mv^2$$

The value of E_k is measured in joules provided m is in kg and v is in $m\,s^{-1}$.

This formula can be derived from Newton's second law and the equations of motion, but you do not need to be able to do that.

Knowledge check 16

Calculate the kinetic energy of a tennis ball of mass 60 g moving at $40\,m\,s^{-1}$.

Elastic strain energy

We have already seen that the energy stored in a spring that obeys Hooke's law, when extended by an amount Δl, is given by:

$$\text{energy stored} = \frac{1}{2}F\Delta l$$

(This will be covered in more detail later in this guide, in the section on materials.)

Knowledge check 17

An elastic band obeys Hooke's law and requires a force of 5.0 N to extend it by 10 cm. Calculate the elastic strain energy stored in the band.

Application of energy conservation

We can use the conservation of energy to calculate the speed of a falling object. For example, if there is no air resistance, an object falling through a height Δh will lose gravitational potential energy:

$$\Delta E_p = mg\Delta h$$

The falling object will gain kinetic energy:

$$\Delta E_k = \frac{1}{2}mv^2$$

By the conservation of energy:

$$\Delta E_p = \Delta E_k$$

Therefore, assuming no other energy losses:

$$mg\Delta h = \frac{1}{2}mv^2 \Rightarrow v = \sqrt{2g\Delta h}$$

Exam tip

It is often much easier to use the principle of conservation of energy in questions that require you to work out the velocity of a falling object than to use equations of motion.

Worked example

A diver dives from a 10 m diving board. Calculate the speed at which he enters the water.

Answer

By the conservation of energy:

$$mg\Delta h = \frac{1}{2}mv^2$$

$$\Rightarrow v = \sqrt{2g\Delta h} = \sqrt{2 \times 9.8 \times 10} = 14\,\mathrm{m\,s^{-1}}$$

In many real situations, there will be work done against a resistive force, for example friction. The work done will be given by $\Delta W = F\Delta x$, assuming that the resistive force is constant. In some cases, however, such as air resistance, this is not the case and the resistive force depends on the velocity of the object.

Worked example

A roller coaster car at a funfair is stationary at the top of a hill before it plunges down into a dip, as shown in Figure 34.

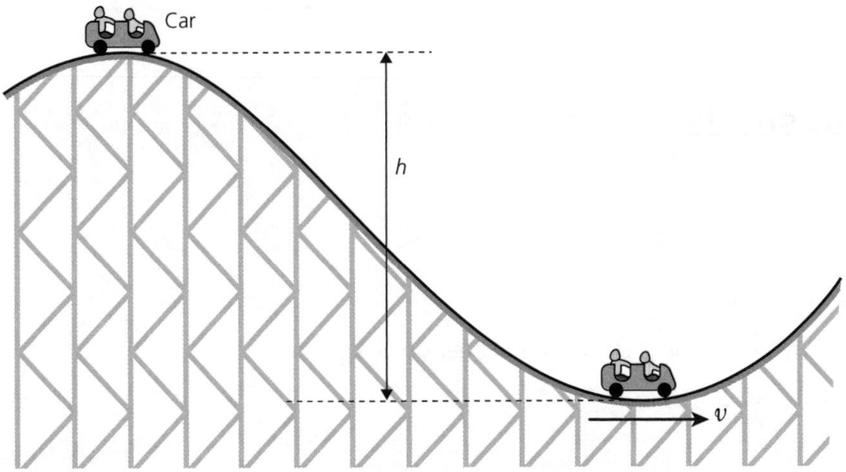

Figure 34 A funfair ride

a If h is 15 m, show that the speed of the car at the lowest point should be about 17.2 m s^{-1}.

b The speed of the car is measured to be 14 m s^{-1} at the lowest point. The total mass of the car and passengers is 500 kg. Show that the kinetic energy lost is about 25 kJ.

c The length of track between the top and bottom of the dip is 25 m. Show that the average frictional force is about 1000 N.

➜

Answers

a By the conservation of energy:

$$mg\Delta h = \frac{1}{2}mv^2$$

$$\Rightarrow v = \sqrt{2g\Delta h} = \sqrt{2 \times 9.8 \times 15} = 17.15\,\text{ms}^{-1}$$

b $\Delta E_k = \left(\frac{1}{2} \times 500 \times 17.15^2\right) - \left(\frac{1}{2} \times 500 \times 14^2\right) = 24500\,\text{J} \approx 25\,\text{kJ}$

c $\Delta W = F \times \Delta x$

$$\Rightarrow \text{F} = \frac{\Delta W}{\Delta t} = \frac{24500}{25} = 980\,\text{N} \approx 1000\,\text{N}$$

Exam tip

When answering 'show that' questions, always give your answer to at least one more significant figure than the value given in the question, to show that you have actually done the calculation.

Summary

After studying this topic you should:

- understand that energy is conserved
- be able to calculate changes in gravitational potential energy
- be able to calculate the kinetic energy of a moving object
- be able to use the conservation of energy to solve problems involving transfer of energy

Materials

Bulk properties of solids

Density

You should recall from GCSE that the density of a material is defined as:

$$\text{density} = \frac{\text{mass}}{\text{volume}}$$

As the unit of mass is kg and the unit of volume is m^3, the unit of density is $kg\,m^{-3}$.

Density is usually given the symbol ρ (Greek letter 'rho'), so we get:

$$\rho = \frac{m}{v}$$

However, you may be more familiar with values of density being given in $g\,cm^{-3}$. To convert from $g\,cm^{-3}$ to $kg\,m^{-3}$, you simply multiply by 10^3.

Density is a useful quantity for comparing the masses of equal volumes of materials. Densities vary considerably, but you may be asked to make estimates in questions so you should have an idea of some densities to the nearest order of magnitude. Table 2 gives some common materials with their densities.

Material	Density/kg m^{-3}	Density to nearest order of magnitude/kg m^{-3}
Air (at normal atmospheric pressure and 20°C)	1.2	1
Water (at 4°C)	1000	10^3
Ice (at 0°C)	992	10^3
Steel (depending on the exact composition)	7800	10^4

Table 2

Water is an unusual substance in that the solid, ice, is less dense than the liquid, which reaches its maximum density at 4°C.

Knowledge check 18

Why does a hot-air balloon rise?

Knowledge check 19

Why do icebergs float?

Hooke's law

An elastic material is one that returns to its original shape after a force is removed. A spring is an example of something that can be described as elastic.

When a spring is loaded it will extend, as shown in Figure 35.

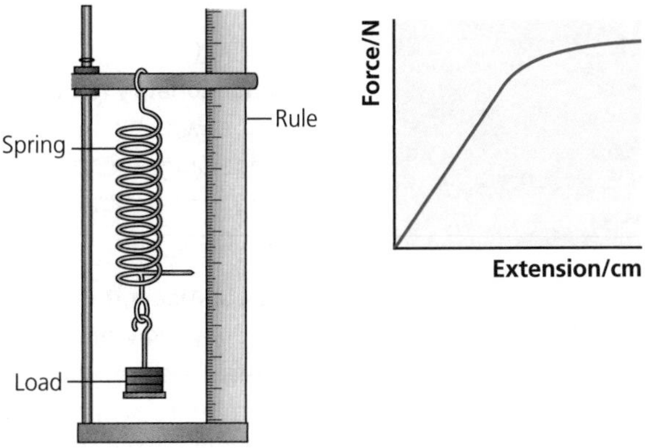

Figure 35 Demonstration of Hooke's law

This graph is a typical force–extension graph for a spring. Initially, the line is straight and force is proportional to extension for the spring:

$$F \propto \Delta l$$

The constant of proportionality is called the spring constant, k, or the stiffness of the spring so that:

$$F = k\Delta l$$

The value of k has the units of N m^{-1} if F is measured in N and Δl in m. It is equal to the gradient of the initial straight part of the graph. A graph for a less stiff material would have a smaller gradient than the one shown.

Two similar springs connected in series will extend twice as far for the same force, so the spring constant of this arrangement, k_s, will be half that for a single spring. In general:

$$k_s = \frac{k}{n}$$

where n is the number of similar springs in series.

Exam tip

Do not forget that Δl is the extension of the spring or material from its original length, not the overall length.

Two similar springs in parallel will require twice the force to extend the arrangement by the same amount, so the spring constant of this arrangement, k_p, will be twice that for a single spring. In general:

$$k_p = nk$$

where n is the number of similar springs in parallel.

Hooke's law states that $F = k\Delta l$. Any material that extends or compresses with force proportional to the extension or compression is said to obey Hooke's law. Figure 36 shows a demonstration of a length of copper wire being stretched.

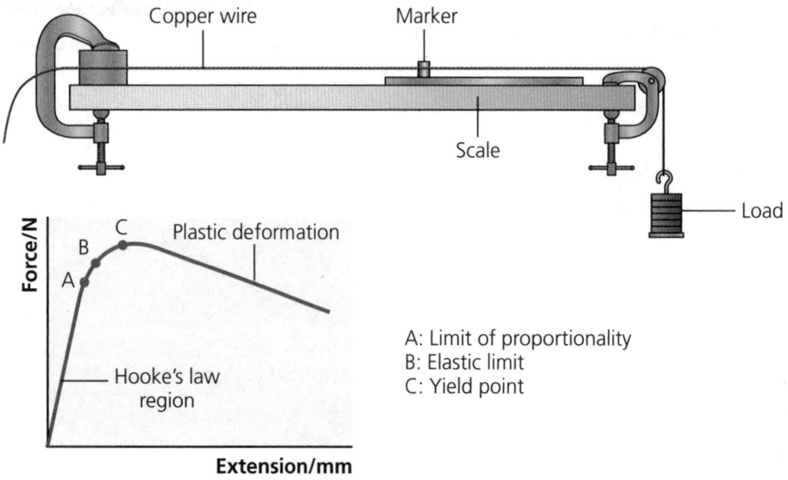

Figure 36 Stretching a length of copper wire

The point at which the graph starts to curve is called the **limit of proportionality**.

Once the load becomes too large, a spring will not return to its original length once the load is removed. It will have a permanent extension. The load at which this just starts to happen is called the **elastic limit**.

Many materials, especially metals, will obey Hooke's law for small loads. Beyond the elastic limit, the material will often stretch and will not return to its original length when the load is removed.

With further increasing load, the material will increase its length significantly. This is known as **plastic deformation**. In a metal, this occurs when layers of atoms slide over each other. The point at which plastic deformation, or plastic flow, starts is called the yield point. This is shown in Figure 36.

When plastic deformation happens, very little force is needed to produce a large extension of a thin wire. When the load is removed, the material will stop stretching but will have a permanent extension. When it is loaded again, the initial force–extension line will be parallel to the original line. This is shown in Figure 37.

Knowledge check 20

A spring of length 25 cm extends by 5.0 cm when a load of 4.0 N is hung on it.

a What is the extension when a load of 9.5 N is hung on the spring?

b What is the total length of the spring now?

Assume the spring obeys Hooke's law.

The **limit of proportionality** is the point at which a force–extension graph stops being a straight line from the origin.

The **elastic limit** is the point beyond which the material will no longer return to its original shape when the force is removed.

Plastic deformation is what happens when the layers of atoms in a material slide over each other and the applied force causes further permanent extension.

Exam tip

Do not confuse the elastic limit with the limit of proportionality. They are often different points.

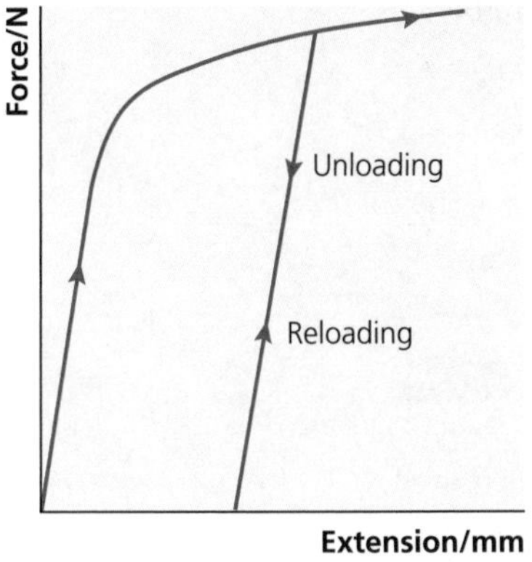

Figure 37 Loading and unloading a metal wire

In some materials, especially ceramics, the atomic bonding is such that layers of atoms cannot slide over each other and plastic deformation cannot take place. Instead, even very small cracks or scratches result in additional stress in the material and it may **fracture** or break easily. Such a material is said to be **brittle**.

Fracture is when a crack extends through a material and the material breaks.

A **brittle** material is one that is not able to deform plastically and fractures when it reaches the yield point.

Elastic strain energy

As already seen in the previous section, the elastic strain energy stored in a stretched material is equal to the work done to stretch the material and is given by the area under a force–extension graph, as shown in Figure 38.

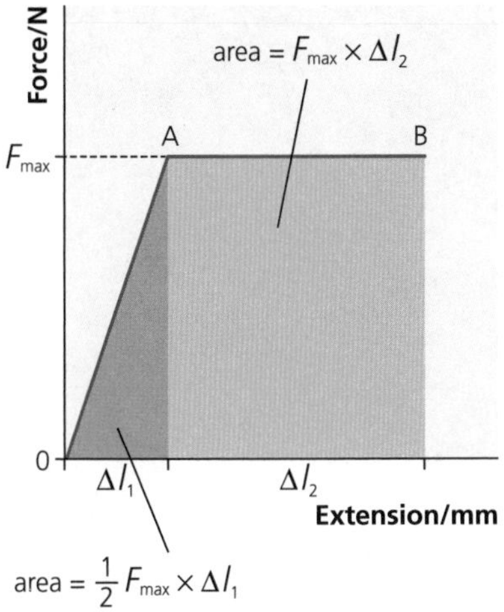

Figure 38 Elastic strain energy stored in a stretched material

For the part of the graph where the material obeys Hooke's law, the elastic strain energy is given by:

$$\text{energy stored} = \frac{1}{2}F\Delta l$$

Since $F = k\Delta l$, this can also be written as:

$$\text{energy stored} = \frac{1}{2}k(\Delta l)^2$$

where Δl is the extension of the material.

For a real material, the graph will not level out to a horizontal line. The area has to be estimated by counting the squares under the graph.

The elastic strain energy stored will be given by the area:

$$\frac{1}{2}F_{max}\Delta l_1$$

The energy required to deform the material will be given by the area:

$$\frac{1}{2}F_{max}\Delta l_2$$

This energy will not be recovered when the load is removed.

Worked example

Looking at Figure 39, estimate the work done to stretch the material up to 6 mm.

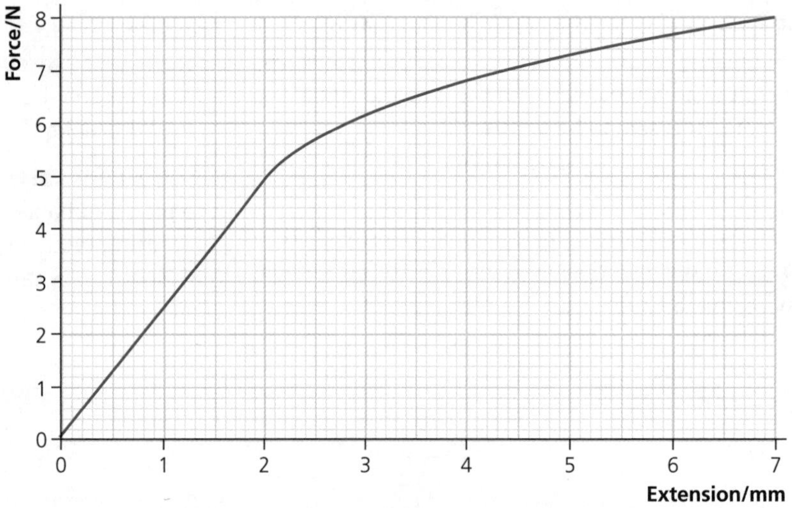

Figure 39

Answer

The area of the Hooke's law region is:

$$\frac{1}{2}F\Delta l = \frac{1}{2} \times 5 \times (2 \times 10^{-3}) = 5 \times 10^{-3}\,\text{J}$$

The area under the graph between 2 mm and 6 mm, when the material is being deformed, is approximately 55 '5 × 5' squares.

each '5 × 5' square = $1 \times 0.5 \times 10^{-3} = 5 \times 10^{-4}$ J

work done for this part = $55 \times 5 \times 10^{-4} = 2.8 \times 10^{-2}$ J

total work done = $5 \times 10^{-3} + 2.8 \times 10^{-2} = 3.3 \times 10^{-2}$ J

The elastic strain energy stored in a material can be partially converted to kinetic energy and then maybe to gravitational potential energy.

Worked example

A catapult is set to fire a pellet of mass 10 g. It is stretched back by 10 cm with a force of 30 N and then released. Assume that the elastic obeys Hooke's law.

a Calculate the maximum possible velocity of the pellet as it leaves the catapult.

The catapult is then pointed directly upwards and released.

b Calculate the maximum possible height reached by the pellet.

Answers

a elastic strain energy stored = $\frac{1}{2} \times 30 \times 0.10 = 1.5\,\text{J}$

$\Delta E_k = 1.5\,\text{J}$, therefore $v^2 = \frac{2 \times \Delta E_k}{m} = \frac{2 \times 1.5}{0.01} = 300 \Rightarrow v = 17\,\text{m}\,\text{s}^{-1}$

b $\Delta E_p = 1.5\,\text{J}$, therefore $\Delta h = \frac{\Delta E_p}{m \times g} = \frac{1.5}{0.01 \times 9.8} = 15\,\text{m}$

Energy conservation in transport design

Conservation of energy is an important consideration in transport design. For example, electric cars are designed so that when slowing down, instead of wasting energy as heat to the surroundings, the electric motors can be used as generators to recover some of the kinetic energy and recharge the battery. Some electric trains, including underground trains, also use this same system to recover energy. A saving of 17% of energy use has been claimed when using this system.

Underground train stations are sometimes built so that the approach to a station is on an upward incline. This helps with the braking by slowing the train on its approach, converting kinetic energy to gravitational potential energy. After the train has stopped and all the passengers have boarded, it has to accelerate away from the station. This requires several megawatts of power from the supply, but the power required can be reduced by having a downward slope out of the station. This allows the gravitational potential energy gained when entering the station to be converted back into kinetic energy as the train leaves the station.

Various vehicles, including Formula 1 cars, rally cars and some buses, feature a kinetic energy recovery system (KERS) which stores kinetic energy in a rotating flywheel or as electrical energy in a battery. This stored energy can then be used to accelerate the vehicle, which can save energy and give greater acceleration than would otherwise be possible – important for a racing car.

Summary

After studying this topic you should:
- be able to calculate density and make estimates involving mass, volume and density
- be able to use Hooke's law to calculate the extension or compression of various spring systems
- know and be able to use the terms stiffness, limit of proportionality, elastic limit, plastic deformation, breaking stress, fracture and brittle
- be able to calculate or estimate the area under a force–extension graph to find the elastic strain energy stored and the energy required to deform a material
- understand why energy conservation is important in transport design

The Young modulus

Tensile stress and tensile strain

A material that is stretched is described as being under tension. Stretching forces are described as tensile forces.

The problem with the spring constant, *k*, is that not only will it be different for every material but it will also vary for different shapes of a given material. This is because, for the same applied tensile force, a sample with a bigger cross-sectional area (with the same length) will extend less, and a longer sample (with the same area) will extend more than the original. The breaking force will also depend on the cross-sectional area of the material.

Structural designers and engineers need to start from knowledge of the physical properties of the materials they wish to use, rather than the properties of particular components. It is possible to take the cross-sectional area and the original length into account so that only dimensions and material properties are needed in order to determine how much a specimen will stretch, or when it will break.

Tensile stress is force divided by cross-sectional area. It has the unit $N\,m^{-2}$ or Pa.

Tensile strain is extension divided by original length and has no unit.

Tensile stress is the tensile force over cross-sectional area:

$$\sigma = \frac{F}{A}$$

As the unit of force is N and the unit of area is m^2, the unit of tensile stress is $N\,m^{-2}$ or Pa (pascal).

Tensile strain is the extension over original length:

$$\varepsilon = \frac{\Delta l}{l}$$

Tensile strain does not have a unit as it is a ratio of lengths. It is usually expressed as a percentage.

When a material is put under stress, it experiences strain.

Knowledge check 21

A stress is applied to a 3.0 m length of wire which undergoes a strain of 1.3%. What is the new length of the wire?

Using stress–strain graphs to find the Young modulus

A graph of stress against strain (see Figure 41 on p. 43) looks similar to a force against extension graph except that it will have the same line for any sample of a given material.

Exam tip

If strain is given as a percentage, you must convert it to a fraction before using it in any calculation.

The gradient of the straight part of the graph is the stiffness of the material (not just the stiffness of the sample). This stiffness of the material is called the Young modulus, E, and has the unit $\mathrm{N\,m^{-2}}$ or Pa.

$$\text{Young modulus} = \frac{\text{stress}}{\text{strain}}$$

$$\frac{\sigma}{\varepsilon} = \frac{F/A}{\Delta l/l} = \frac{Fl}{A\Delta l}$$

The breaking stress is the stress at which a material breaks.

Exam tip

You should be able to describe how to measure the Young modulus of a wire.

Required practical 4

Determination of the Young modulus by a simple method

The Young modulus of a wire can be measured with an experimental arrangement such as the one shown in Figure 40.

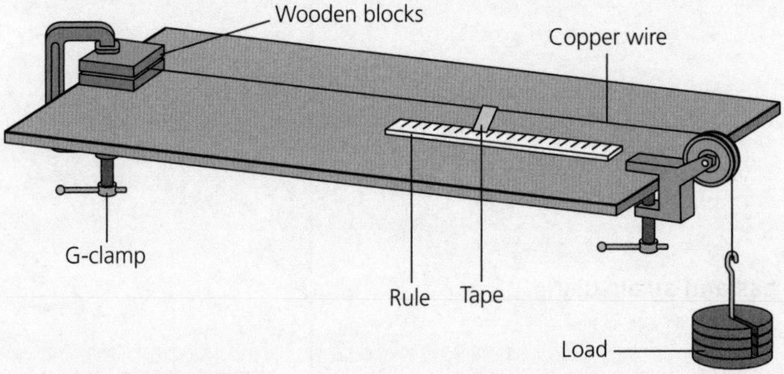

Figure 40 Measuring the Young modulus and breaking stress of copper wire. Do not forget to wear safety goggles when carrying out this experiment

The radius of the wire should be measured in several places using a micrometer and the original length, from the wooden blocks to the tape marker, should also be measured before the experiment is started. Once the wire starts to plastically deform, the diameter will reduce so it is a good idea to re-measure the diameter each time the wire stretches significantly. This allows the true stress to be calculated.

In one experiment, the original diameter of the wire, d, was measured six times with a micrometer. The readings obtained are shown in Table 3.

Diameter/mm	0.25	0.25	0.26	0.26	0.27	0.25

Table 3

You should calculate a mean value for the diameter and the cross-sectional area in m^2. In this case, the mean value of d is 0.257 mm and a calculation of the cross-sectional area gives:

$A = 5.19 \times 10^{-8}\,\mathrm{m^2}$

The range of results for this diameter is between 0.25 mm and 0.27 mm, which is a range of 0.02 mm.

➜

The spread, which is half the range, is ±0.01 mm and this is one measure of the uncertainty in the value of *d*.

Thus, the percentage uncertainty in *d* and in the radius, *r*, is:

$$\frac{\Delta d}{d} \times 100\% = \frac{0.01}{0.257} \times 100\% = 3.9\%$$

Since area, *A*, is equal to $\pi \times r^2$, the percentage uncertainty in *A* is 2× the percentage uncertainty in *r* which is 7.8%. This is likely to be the most significant uncertainty in the calculation of stress.

In the same experiment to measure the Young modulus of a wire, the original length of the wire, *l*, is 2.2 m and the average results obtained for force and extension are shown in Table 4.

Force/N	Extension/mm
0.0	0.00
2.0	0.73
4.0	1.46
5.8	2.19
8.0	4.00
9.0	6.66
9.8	13.00

Table 4

You can use these data to calculate the stress and strain using:

$$\text{stress} = \frac{F}{A}$$

$$\text{strain} = \frac{\Delta l}{l}$$

You can then plot a graph of stress against strain for the wire.

Depending on your own experimental arrangement to measure Δl, the uncertainty in this measurement could be quite large, ±0.5 mm for example. For the larger values of extension, this is not very significant but it is likely to be significant for smaller values of extension and therefore the smaller values of strain.

The gradient of the initial straight line is equal to the Young modulus of copper.

From the graph, you should be able to calculate that the Young modulus, *E*, is approximately:

$$E = \frac{\Delta \sigma}{\Delta \varepsilon} = \frac{117 \times 10^6}{0.001} = 1.17 \times 10^{11}\,\text{Pa} \approx 120\,\text{GPa}$$

If the wire is then loaded further until it breaks, the graph can be extended to show the breaking stress. This is shown in Figure 41 but, because it shows the whole extension of the wire up to the point where it breaks, it is more difficult to measure the gradient of the first part of the graph accurately.

From the graph, the breaking stress for copper wire is about 225 MPa.

The dotted line shows what would happen if the copper wire were to be unloaded after it had deformed plastically. This would result in a permanent strain once all the loads were removed.

Exam tip

If you are told to plot stress against strain, this means putting stress on the *y*-axis and strain on the *x*-axis.

Exam tip

You should be able to describe how a material behaves from its stress–strain graph, using the correct technical terminology.

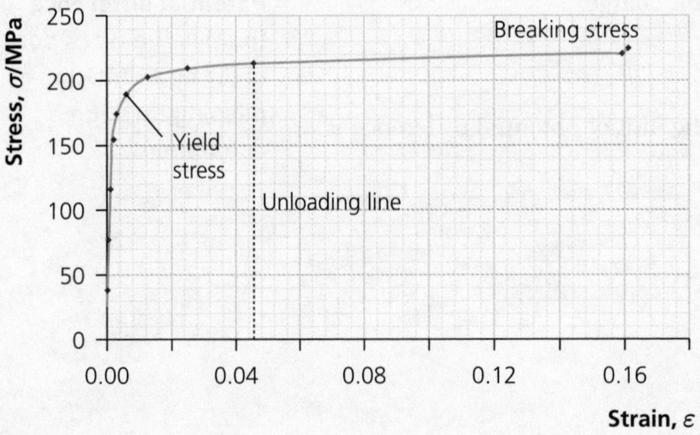

Figure 41 Stress–strain curve for a copper wire

Summary

After studying this topic you should:

- know and be able to use the terms tensile stress and tensile strain
- know how to measure stress and strain for a stretched material
- be able to calculate the Young modulus from a stress–strain graph

Electricity

Current electricity

Basics of electricity

An electric current is a flow of charge. In a metallic conductor, this is a movement of electrons, but it can also be a flow of ions or positive charges in other conductors. The unit of charge is the coulomb (C). The charge on one electron is -1.6×10^{-19} C which means that it requires 6.25×10^{18} electrons to make a charge of 1 C.

In order to make charge flow, work has to be done on the charge. This work is done by a potential difference.

When charges flow in a circuit, they will do work on the material because of the resistance in the circuit.

Current, I, is the rate of flow of charge, Q:

$$I = \frac{\Delta Q}{\Delta t}$$

As the unit of charge is C and the unit of time is s, the unit of current is C s^{-1} or A (ampere).

Current is the rate of flow of charge.

Potential difference (p.d.), V, is the work done per unit charge:

$$V = \frac{W}{Q}$$

As the unit of work is J and the unit of charge is C, the unit of potential difference is $J\,C^{-1}$ or V (volt).

Resistance, R, is defined as:

$$R = \frac{V}{I}$$

The unit of resistance is Ω (ohm).

Potential difference (p.d.) is the work done on or by a unit charge passing through a component.

Worked example

a Show that in 30 s, a charge of 45 C passes through a resistor when a current of 1.5 A flows.

b Calculate the number of electrons that pass through the resistor in that time.

The potential difference across the resistor is 5.0 V.

c Calculate the resistance of the resistor.

d How much energy would be transferred to heat energy in the surroundings by the resistor in 30 s?

e Calculate the power transferred.

Answers

a $I = \frac{\Delta Q}{\Delta t}$

$\Rightarrow \Delta Q = I\Delta t = 1.5 \times 30 = 45\text{C}$

b $\frac{45}{1.6 \times 10^{-19}} = 2.8 \times 10^{20}$ electrons

c $R = \frac{V}{I} = \frac{5.0}{1.5} = 3.3\,\Omega$

d 45 C pass through the resistor and each coulomb does 5.0 J of work. Thus, the energy transferred is:

$45 \times 5.0 = 225\,\text{J}$

e power $= \frac{\Delta W}{\Delta t} = \frac{225}{30} = 7.5\,\text{W}$

Summary

After studying this topic you should:

- know the definitions for current and potential difference
- be able to measure the resistance of a component

Current–voltage characteristics

The behaviour of components in an electrical circuit can be shown by plotting the current through the component against the potential difference across the component. Such plots show the *characteristics* of the component.

A conductor that obeys **Ohm's law** is said to be ohmic. Metallic conductors and some non-metallic conductors are ohmic. Ohm's law is not simply that:

$$R = \frac{V}{I}$$

This formula is always true, whether or not the material obeys Ohm's law. Ohm's law applies to the special case of constant physical conditions.

It is often easiest to see if a component is ohmic by looking at the current–potential difference graph or characteristics of the component. Some examples are shown in Figure 42.

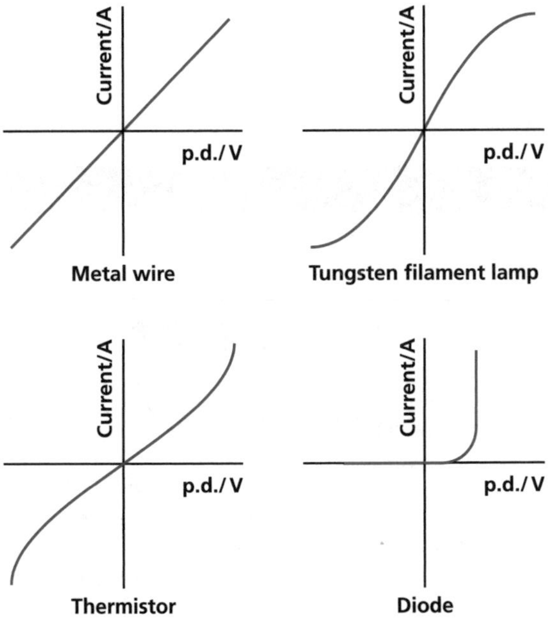

Figure 42 Current-potential difference graphs for some components

The characteristic for the metal wire is a straight line through the origin. This indicates that, over the range of values tested, current is directly proportional to the potential difference, $I \propto V$.

The filament lamp and thermistor have linear sections showing that they both obey Ohm's law for a limited range of values, but beyond these values the temperature does not remain constant and the resistance changes. In the case of the filament lamp, increasing temperature means increasing resistance.

A diode behaves differently depending on which way it is connected in the circuit. In one direction, it starts to conduct after a certain potential difference is applied across it. When connected in the other direction, it does not conduct for the same range of

Ohm's law states that the current through a conductor is directly proportional to the potential difference across the conductor, provided that the temperature and other physical conditions are kept constant.

Exam tip

You might be given component characteristic graphs with current on the *x*-axis and potential difference on the *y*-axis, so make sure you can recognise the curves drawn with the axes either way round.

potential differences. It is because some components behave differently depending on the sign of the applied potential difference that characteristics of components are shown with both positive and negative values.

The characteristics of a component are determined using an ammeter, a voltmeter and a variable power supply, as shown in Figure 43. You can assume that the ammeter has zero resistance and the voltmeter has infinite resistance. The use of modern digital meters means that these are reasonable assumptions.

Knowledge check 22

Sketch the current–p.d. characteristics of a tungsten filament lamp with current on the x-axis and potential difference on the y-axis.

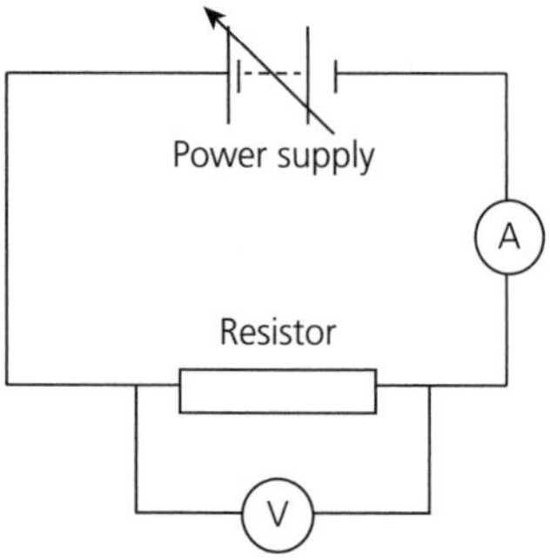

Figure 43 Apparatus for measuring the characteristics of a component

Summary

After studying this topic you should:

- know the definition for Ohm's law
- recognise the characteristics of different components in a circuit

Resistivity

The resistance of a conductor depends on the length, the cross-sectional area and the material of the conductor. Two wires of the same length with the same thickness can have very different resistances if they are made from different materials.

We use a quantity called resistivity, ρ, which is the resistance of a piece of material of unit length and unit cross-sectional area:

$$\rho = \frac{RA}{l}$$

Where A is the cross-sectional area in m^2, l is the length in m and R is the resistance in Ω. Therefore, the unit of resistivity is Ω m.

Exam tip

Note the unit of resistivity. It is a common error to think it is ohm *per* metre but this is not the case. It is ohm metre (Ω m).

Knowledge check 23

Show that the unit of resistivity is the ohm metre.

Worked example

A piece of copper wire of length 5.0 m has a diameter of 0.24 mm. It has a resistance of 1.9 Ω. Calculate the resistivity of copper.

Answer

cross-sectional area, $A = \pi r^2 = \pi \times (0.12 \times 10^{-3})^2 = 4.5 \times 10^{-8}\,m^2$

$$\rho = \frac{RA}{l} = \frac{1.9 \times 4.5 \times 10^{-8}}{5.0} = 1.7 \times 10^{-8}\,\Omega\,m$$

Exam tip

Note that all the data in the question are to two significant figures, so your answer should also be given to two significant figures.

Required practical 5

Determination of resistivity of a wire using a micrometer, ammeter and voltmeter

To measure the resistivity of a wire, it is necessary to measure the resistance of different lengths of the wire. A suitable experimental arrangement is shown in Figure 44. A piece of nichrome wire is taped to a metre rule and a pair of crocodile clips are used to connect it to an electric circuit. Take care with these connections or they can introduce systematic errors into your data.

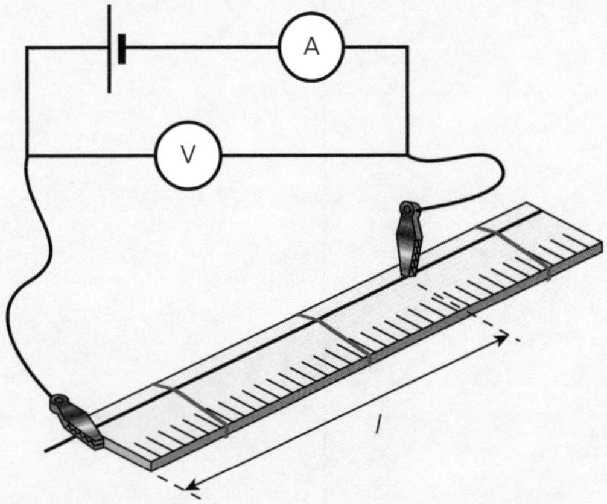

Figure 44 Measuring the resistivity of a wire

A voltmeter and ammeter are used to measure the potential difference across the wire and the current through the wire. It helps to use a small screwdriver or a special device called a jockey to touch on the wire. Do not press too hard or the wire will be damaged and the resistance changed. The diameter of the wire should be measured at several points and an average taken. A wire of different diameter can also be used and the resistivities compared.

Rearranging the formula for resistivity:

$$\rho = \frac{RA}{l} \Rightarrow R = \frac{\rho}{A} \times l$$

If you plot a graph of resistance against length, it should be a straight line with gradient ρ/A.

An experiment to measure the resistivity of two pieces of wire of the same material but different diameters (32 swg and 30 swg, swg being standard wire gauge) gives the results shown in Table 5.

		Current/A	
Length/m	p.d./V	32 swg	30 swg
0.00	3.0	0.00	0.00
0.10	3.0	1.64	2.16
0.20	3.0	0.82	1.08
0.30	3.0	0.55	0.72
0.40	3.0	0.41	0.54
0.50	3.0	0.33	0.43

		Current/A	
Length/m	p.d./V	32 swg	30 swg
0.60	3.0	0.27	0.31
0.70	3.0	0.23	0.31
0.80	3.0	0.20	0.27
0.90	3.0	0.18	0.24
1.00	3.0	0.16	0.22

Table 5

→

Using these data, you can calculate the resistance for each wire for each different length. A resistance–length graph of results is shown in Figure 45.

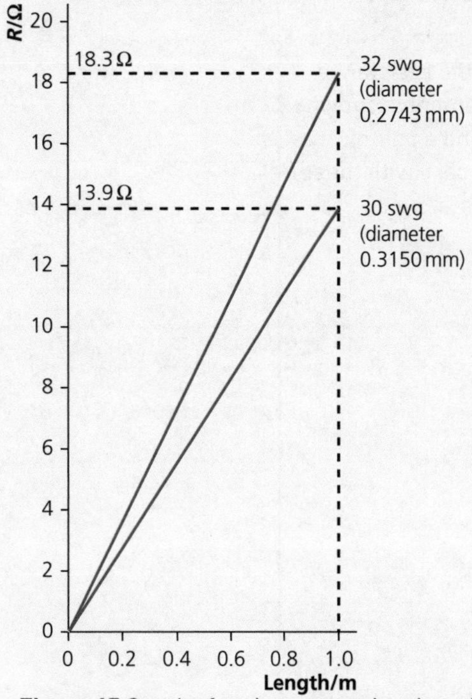

Figure 45 Graph of resistance against length for different wires

Taking the 32 swg wire, the diameter is 0.2743 mm and therefore the cross-sectional area is:

$$A=\frac{\pi d^2}{4}=\frac{\pi\times\left(0.2743\times10^{-3}\right)^2}{4}=5.91\times10^{-8}\,\text{m}^2$$

The gradient of the graph is:

$$\frac{1.83}{1.00}=18.3\,\Omega\,\text{m}^{-1}$$

Therefore:

resistivity, ρ = gradient × A = $18.3 \times 5.91 \times 10^{-8} = 1.1 \times 10^{-6}\,\Omega\,\text{m}$

This is close to the accepted value for the resistivity of nichrome.

The value can be checked by calculating the resistivity of the second piece of wire.

Exam tip

You should be able to describe how to measure the resistivity of the material for a length of wire.

Resistance and temperature

For most materials, resistance does not stay constant with temperature change. Depending on the material, the resistance either increases or decreases with increasing temperature.

All conductors have mobile charge carriers. In metals, these are 'free' electrons. In semiconductors, these are electrons and holes, and in other materials the mobile charge carriers can be positive or negative ions or electrons. In all cases, increasing the temperature of a material frees more charge carriers to take part in conduction. This will tend to decrease resistance as temperature increases.

However, in a solid conductor, increasing temperature also has the effect of increasing the vibration of the atoms in the material lattice, which increases the interaction between the mobile charge carriers and the lattice atoms. This will tend to increase resistance as temperature increases.

In metals, this second mechanism is dominant so the resistivity of a metal, and therefore the resistance, increases with temperature. This can be seen in Figure 42 (page 45) where the resistance of the tungsten filament lamp is seen to increase as the current increases (and the filament becomes hotter).

In most semiconductors, the first mechanism is dominant so increased temperature results in decreased resistivity. This is used in negative temperature coefficient (NTC) thermistors and can also be seen in Figure 42, where the resistance of the thermistor decreases with increasing current (and the thermistor becomes hotter).

Some materials that we regard as insulators can become conductors at high temperatures because the temperature is high enough to allow some charge carriers to become mobile, for example in glass.

Both metals and semiconductors can be used as temperature sensors. Platinum resistance thermometers are often used and have the advantage that, over a limited range of temperatures, there is an almost linear relationship between resistivity and temperature.

The resistance of a thermistor changes considerably over a range of temperatures but the relationship is non-linear. A typical relationship between resistance and temperature for a thermistor is shown in Figure 46.

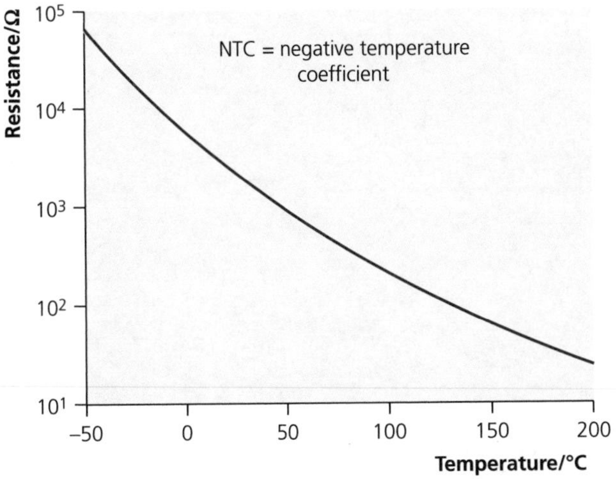

Figure 46 Typical variation of resistance with temperature for a thermistor. Note that the resistance scale is logarithmic because of the very large change in resistance with temperature

Knowledge check 24

Using Figure 46, estimate the temperature at which the resistance of the thermistor is:

a 10 000 Ω **c** 100 Ω
b 1000 Ω **d** 30 Ω

Thermistors are used as temperature sensors, usually as part of a potential divider circuit (which will be covered later in this guide). The non-linearity of resistance with temperature means that the circuit often has to be able to map a value of temperature to a value of resistance. This can be done easily with digital circuits but initially a calibration curve needs to be produced. The experimental arrangement to do this is shown in Figure 47.

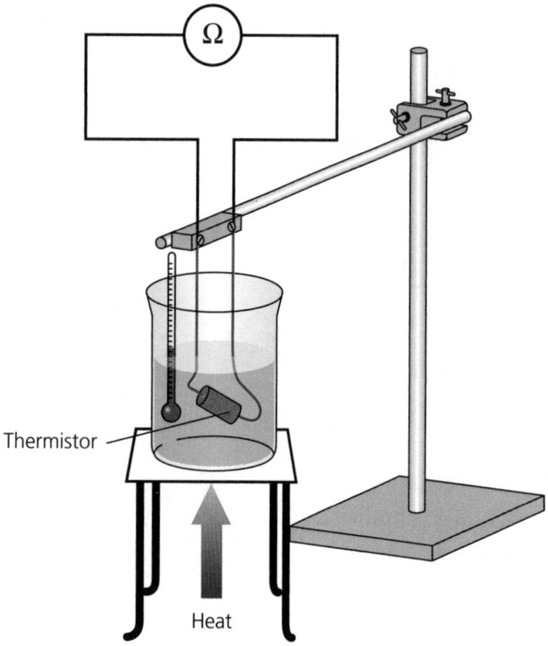

Figure 47 Experimental arrangement for calibrating a thermistor

A typical set of data for this experiment is shown in Table 6.

Temperature/°C	Resistance/Ω
20	341
30	259
40	197
50	154
60	120
70	90
80	68
90	52
100	42

Table 6 Resistance and temperature for a typical thermistor

You could try this experiment for yourself. You can start at a lower temperature than 20°C by adding ice to cold water. Take care that the heat from the Bunsen burner does not damage the thermistor leads. Remember to wear safety goggles and do not touch the retort stand or beaker once heating has started.

A graph of resistance against temperature should look like Figure 48.

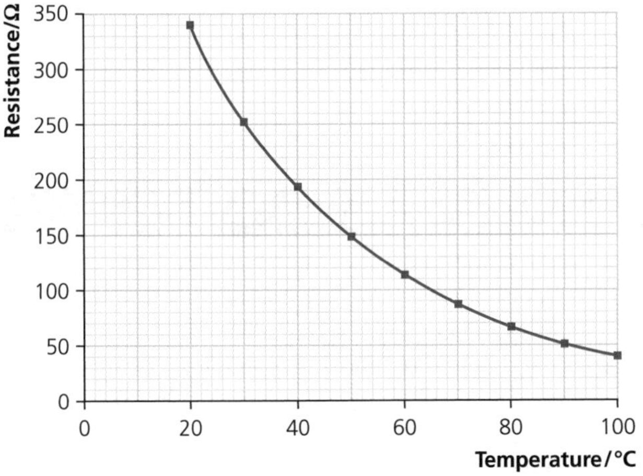

Figure 48 Graph of resistance against temperature for a thermistor

You could also try to plot a graph of natural log R against temperature. You would find that this gives a straight line, indicating that the resistance of a thermistor is of the form:

$$R_\theta = R_0 e^{-k\theta}$$

where R_θ is the resistance at θ°C, R_0 is the resistance at 0°C and k is a constant.

Knowledge check 25

If you are taking A-level, plot a graph of natural log R against temperature for the data in Table 6 and determine the resistance at 0°C and the value of k.

Superconductivity

Resistance is a result of the charge carriers interacting with the atoms in a material. However, for some materials, there is a state where electrons behave differently and do not interact with the atoms in the material lattice, but can pass through the material freely. When this happens all resistance disappears and the material becomes a superconductor.

There is a critical temperature below which superconductivity occurs for a particular material. Some typical critical temperatures are given in Table 7.

Material	Critical temperature/K
Gallium	1.1
Tin	3.7
Mercury	4.2
Lead	7.2
Niobium	9.3
Yttrium-barium-copper oxide	92
Mercury-barium-calcium-copper oxide	133

Table 7 Critical temperatures for superconductivity in some materials

The last two materials in the table are known as 'high temperature' superconductors. Their critical temperatures are not particularly high, 133 K is about –140°C, but this is well above the boiling point of liquid nitrogen, which is about –195°C (77 K), so these materials are superconductors at the temperatures possible with liquid nitrogen. The other materials have to be cooled using liquid helium or liquid hydrogen, and this is more difficult and more expensive.

As superconductors can carry very large currents without producing any heat, they are used to produce the very strong magnetic fields needed for magnetic resonance imaging (MRI) machines in hospitals. Superconductors are also used for transmitting electrical power without energy loss, although their use in this application is limited by the difficulty and expense of keeping the transmission line at a suitably low temperature.

Summary

After studying this topic you should:

- be able to calculate the resistivity of a material given its resistance, length and diameter
- know how to carry out an experiment to measure resistivity
- explain why resistivity changes with temperature for metal conductors and semiconductors
- understand that a thermistor can be used as a temperature sensor and how to obtain a calibration curve for a thermistor
- know that some materials exhibit the property of superconductivity below a critical temperature
- understand some of the applications of superconductors

Circuits

Resistors in series

A series circuit is one in which components are connected one after the other, as shown in Figure 49.

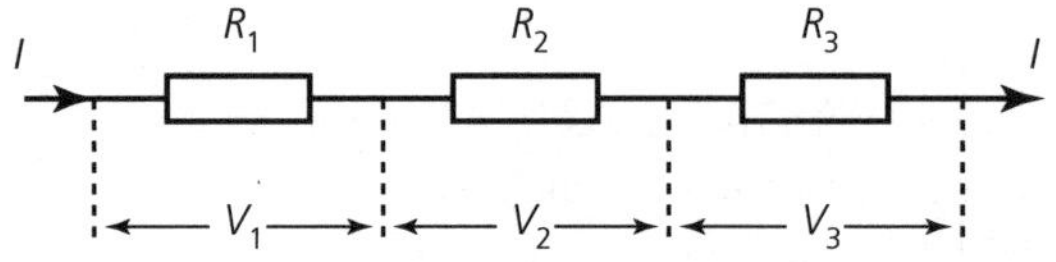

Figure 49 Resistors in series

Both charge and energy must be conserved in all circuits.

In Figure 49, for charge to be conserved, the current, I, through each resistor must be the same. An ammeter placed anywhere in a series circuit will always read the same value.

For energy to be conserved, the total potential difference across all the resistors, V_{total}, must be the sum of all the individual potential differences. Therefore:

$$V_{total} = V_1 + V_2 + V_3$$

Combining this with the formula from the definition of resistance, $V = IR$, we obtain:

$$IR_{total} = IR_1 + IR_2 + IR_3$$

This gives:

$$R_{total} = R_1 + R_2 + R_3$$

where R_{total} is the equivalent single resistance that could replace R_1, R_2 and R_3.

This expression can be extended to any number of resistors in series.

Knowledge check 26

Calculate the resistance of a 12 Ω, 10 Ω and 3 Ω resistor connected in series.

Resistors in parallel

A parallel circuit is one in which two or more components are connected between the same two points, as shown in Figure 50.

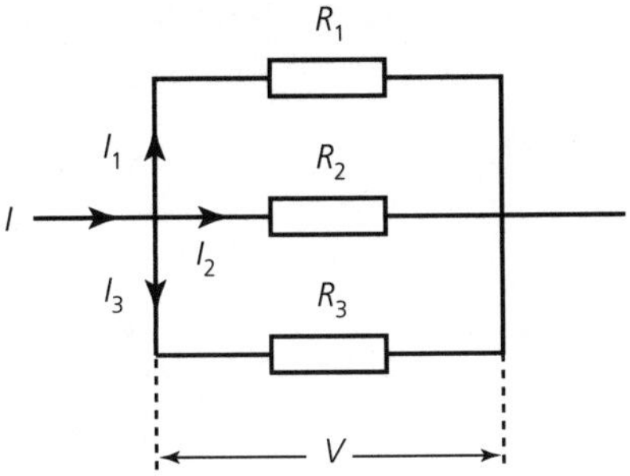

Figure 50 Resistors in parallel

In a parallel circuit, conservation of charge means that the total charge entering a junction must be equal to the total charge leaving that junction. In Figure 50, this means that the total current through the three resistors must be equal to the sum of the current through each individual resistor:

$$I_{total} = I_1 + I_2 + I_3$$

The potential difference across any component connected in parallel must be the same. Since:

$$I = \frac{V}{R}$$

$$\frac{V}{R_{total}} = \frac{V}{R_1} + \frac{V}{R_2} + \frac{V}{R_3}$$

This means that:

$$\frac{1}{R_{total}} = \frac{1}{R_1} + \frac{1}{R_2} + \frac{1}{R_3}$$

As with the case of resistors in series, this formula can be extended to any number of resistors in parallel.

Exam tip

When adding resistances in parallel, the total resistance is always lower than the lowest of the individual resistors in the circuit.

If resistors of equal resistance are in parallel, the total resistance is the value of each resistor divided by the number of resistors in the circuit, for example, three 12 Ω resistors in parallel will have a total resistance of 4 Ω.

Problems involving both series and parallel combinations of resistors should be tackled by calculating the parallel parts first and then adding the series elements.

Knowledge check 27

Calculate the resistance of a 12 Ω, 10 Ω and 3 Ω resistor connected in parallel.

Knowledge check 28

Calculate the total resistance of three 18 Ω resistors in parallel with each other, connected in series with four 20 Ω resistors in parallel with each other.

Worked example

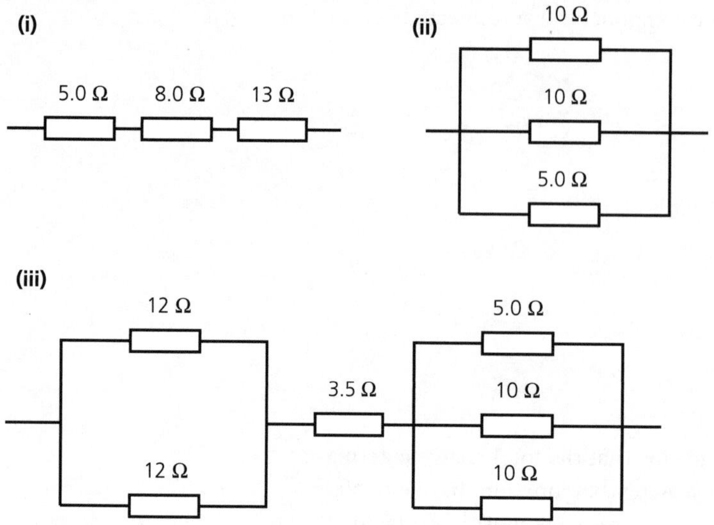

Figure 51

a Calculate the total resistance in circuits (i), (ii) and (iii) in Figure 51.

The total current through the combination in (iii) is 1.5 A.

b i Calculate the potential difference across the total combination in (iii) and across the 3.5 Ω resistor.

ii Calculate the current in one of the 10 Ω resistors.

Answers

a i $5.0 + 8.0 + 13 = 26\,\Omega$

ii $\frac{1}{R_{total}} = \frac{1}{R_1} + \frac{1}{R_2} + \frac{1}{R_3}$

$\Rightarrow \frac{1}{R_{total}} = \frac{1}{10} + \frac{1}{10} + \frac{1}{5} = \frac{4}{10}$

$\Rightarrow R_{total} = \frac{10}{4} = 2.5\ \Omega$

iii Taking the separate parts:

two 12 Ω resistors in parallel (on the left) = 6 Ω

combination on the right is the same as in (ii), $R_{total} = 2.5\,\Omega$

total resistance = 6 + 3.5 + 2.5 = 12 Ω

b i $V = IR = 1.5 \times 12 = 18\,V$ across the total combination

$V = IR = 1.5 \times 3.5 = 5.25\,V$ across the 3.5 Ω resistor

ii The potential difference across the right-hand parallel combination is given by:

$V = IR = 1.5 \times 2.5 = 3.75\,V$

This is the same as across each of the resistors in the parallel combination:

$I = \frac{V}{R} = \frac{3.75}{10} = 0.375\ A$

Energy and power

In a circuit, the energy transferred in a component is equal to the work done per unit charge that passes through that component.

We have already seen that the potential difference is the work done per unit charge:

$$V = \frac{W}{\Delta Q}$$

where ΔQ is the amount of charge passing and W is the work done or energy transferred, E.

Rearranging:

$$E = V\Delta Q$$

Since:

$$I = \frac{\Delta Q}{\Delta t}$$

$$\Rightarrow \Delta Q = I\Delta t$$

Substituting:

$$E = VI\Delta t$$

where E is the energy transferred in time Δt.

In practice, Δt is simply written as t, the time for which the current flows, which gives:

$$E = VIt$$

Worked example

A lamp has a potential difference of 230 V across it and a current of 0.04 A flows through it. It is switched on for 10 hours. Calculate the energy transferred from electrical energy in that time.

Answer

Note that the time must be in seconds so:

$$t = 10 \times 60 \times 60 = 36\,000\,\text{s}$$

$$E = VIt = 230 \times 0.04 \times 36000$$

$$= 3.3 \times 10^5\ \text{J}$$

However, the power dissipated in a component is often the most useful quantity to know. Light bulbs and heaters are sold according to their power and you may see the power of a vacuum cleaner motor quoted on the packaging, for example. Power is defined as:

power = energy transferred per second

$$P = \frac{E}{t} = VI$$

Since:

$$V = IR$$

Exam tip

You will often need to use the alternative versions of the formula for electrical power:

$$P = I^2R \quad \text{or} \quad P = \frac{V^2}{R}$$

the formula for electrical power can also be written as:

$$P = I^2R = \frac{V^2}{R}$$

Worked example

A car headlamp, designed to have a potential difference of 12 V across it, has a resistance of 2.4 Ω. Calculate the power of the lamp at its working voltage.

Answer

$$\text{power} = \frac{V^2}{R} = \frac{12^2}{2.4} = 60\,\text{W}$$

Knowledge check 29

A kettle element dissipates a power of 3.0 kW. Its resistance is 17.8 Ω. Calculate the current that flows through the element when the kettle is working.

Cells in series

A battery is a set of cells, usually connected in series. For example, a 12 V car battery consists of six 2 V cells connected in series. A 6 V battery pack that you might use in the lab will consist of four 1.5 V cells in series, as shown in Figure 52.

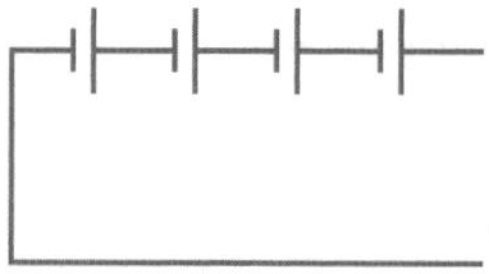

Figure 52 Cells in series

The cells are connected so that the positive terminal of one cell is connected to the negative terminal of the next cell. Conservation of energy means that when cells are connected in series, each cell does work on the charge as it passes through the cell.

In any series circuit, the same charge must pass through each cell in the same time, therefore the total work done per unit charge is the sum of the work done per unit charge for each cell. In other words:

$$V_{total} = V_1 + V_2 + V_3 + \ldots$$

Cells in parallel

It is generally unwise to connect cells in parallel but if they are connected in parallel, they must be identical cells and they must be connected as shown in Figure 53.

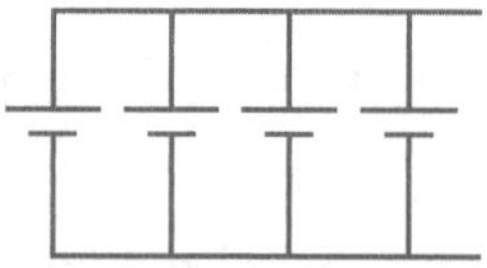

Figure 53 Cells connected in parallel

The positive terminals are connected together and the negative terminals are also connected together. The total potential difference across the arrangement will be the same as for one of the cells, often 1.5 V. As in any parallel circuit, the total current will be divided between the cells. This may have the advantage of increasing the capacity of the battery if only a small potential difference is needed. Mainly it will mean that a larger current is available from this arrangement because the effective internal resistance is reduced. (Internal resistance will be covered later in this guide.)

Knowledge check 30

a Six 1.5 V cells are connected in series. Calculate the total potential difference across all the cells.

b The six cells are now connected in parallel. Calculate the total potential difference across the arrangement.

Summary

After studying this topic you should:

- be able to calculate the equivalent resistance for resistors in series, in parallel and in circuits containing a combination of series and parallel arrangements
- know how to measure the resistance of a component
- understand that energy transfer can be calculated and that power is energy transfer per unit time
- be able to use the equations for energy and power in electrical circuits
- understand that the rules for combining resistors and cells in series and parallel are a result of conservation of energy and conservation of charge

Potential divider

Many sensors change their resistance with a changing input, for example a thermistor, but it is usually necessary to provide a varying potential difference to a circuit for it to be useful.

The way to produce a potential difference that depends on the resistance of a sensor is by using a potential divider circuit.

A **potential divider** consists of two resistors in series, as shown in Figure 54. The potential difference across either of the resistors is determined by the ratio of that resistance to the total resistance.

A **potential divider** is two resistors connected across a supply which allows a proportion of the supply voltage to be tapped off.

The current in a circuit is given by:

$$I = \frac{V}{R}$$

where R is the total resistance and $R = R_1 + R_2$. In addition, at all times $V = V_1 + V_2$. Thus:

$$I = \frac{V}{R_1 + R_2}$$

where V is the input potential difference. This may be 5 V but could be any value.

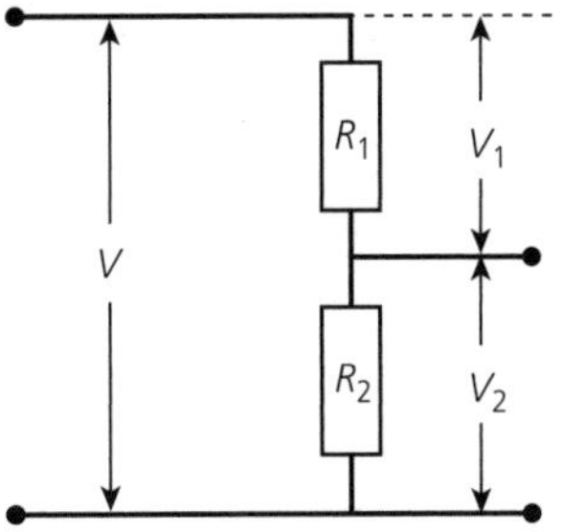

Figure 54 A potential divider circuit

The output potential difference, V_2, across R_2 is given by:

$$V_2 = \frac{R_2}{R_1 + R_2} V$$

If $R_1 + R_2$ remains constant, $V_2 \propto R_2$ and the output potential difference is directly related to the value of the resistance of the sensor, if R_2 is the sensor.

The best example of the potential divider is the potentiometer. Here the resistors R_1 and R_2 are a single resistor with a sliding contact that can be adjusted to connect to any part of the resistor, as shown by the circuit in Figure 55. Figure 56 shows what a potentiometer looks like.

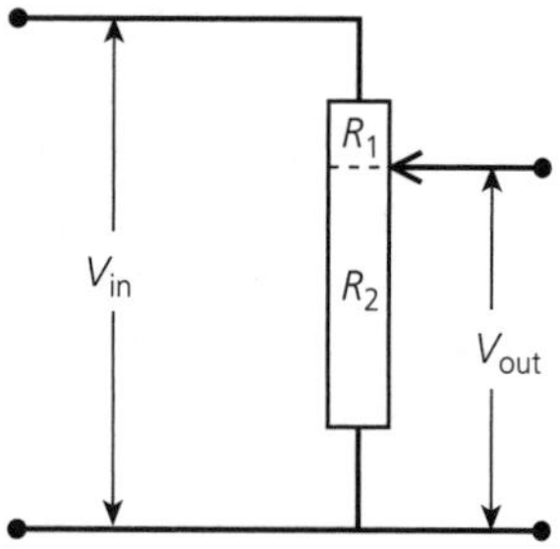

Figure 55 A potentiometer circuit

Figure 56 A potentiometer

In this case, $R_1 + R_2$ is constant because they are part of the same total resistance. Therefore, the output is directly proportional to R_2 and the output potential difference, V_{out}, can vary from 0 to V_{in}:

$$V_{out} = \frac{R_2}{R_1 + R_2} V_{in}$$

This arrangement allows a variable output potential difference from a fixed power supply, although as soon as a load is connected across R_2 this acts as a resistor in parallel to R_2, which means that the output voltage may not be the value expected.

An example of a use of this arrangement is in the volume control of audio equipment where changing the control setting can vary the output volume between zero and maximum volume.

Worked example

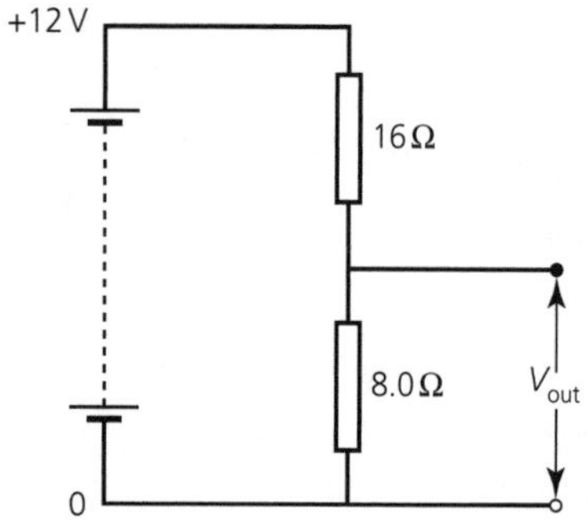

Figure 57

a Calculate the value of V_{out} in Figure 57.

b Calculate the potential difference across the 16 Ω resistor.

Answers

a $V_{out} = \frac{R_2}{R_1 + R_2} V_{in} = \frac{8.0}{16 + 8.0} \times 12 = 4.0\text{ V}$

b Since $V = V_1 + V_2$ then $V_1 = V - V_2 = 12 - 4 = 8.0\text{ V}$

Knowledge check 31

In Figure 55, R_1 is 25 Ω, R_2 is 75 Ω and V_{in} is 10 V. Calculate the value of V_{out}.

Worked example

In Figure 55, the total resistance of the potentiometer is 10 kΩ. The input voltage is 6.0 V and the required output voltage is 5.0 V.

a Calculate the value of R_2.

The potentiometer consists of a piece of resistance wire of length 1.5 m.

b Calculate the position of the sliding contact along the wire.

Answers

a

$$V_{out} = \frac{R_2}{R_1 + R_2} V_{in}$$

$$\Rightarrow 5.0 = \frac{R_2}{10 \times 10^3} \times 6.0$$

$$\Rightarrow R_2 = \frac{5.0 \times 10 \times 10^3}{6.0} = 8.3 \times 10^3 \ \Omega$$

b Assuming the wire is of uniform resistance, the resistance is proportional to the length. Therefore:

$$l_2 = \frac{8.3 \times 10^3}{10 \times 10^3} \times 1.5 = 1.25 \text{ m}$$

A thermistor can be used as a temperature sensor and a light dependent resistor (LDR) can be used to detect light level. For example, a thermistor may be used as part of a switch to turn a heating system on and off, and a LDR may be used as part of a switch to turn on a street light at dusk and turn it off again at dawn.

The resistance of a thermistor varies with temperature and the resistance of an LDR varies with light level. Both can be used in a potential divider circuit, as shown in Figure 58.

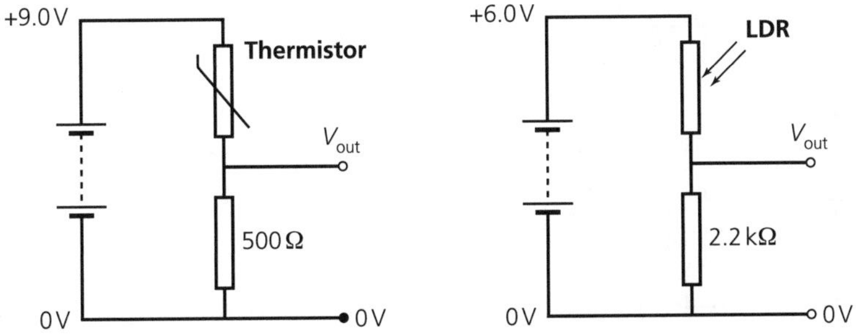

Figure 58 A thermistor and LDR used in a potential divider circuit

For both a thermistor and an LDR, the resistance decreases with increasing input – temperature or light level. Therefore, in order for the output voltage to increase with increasing input, the resistors need to be put as R_1 in the potential divider circuit.

Worked example

The thermistor in Figure 58 has a resistance of 300 Ω at 24°C and 120 Ω at 60°C. Calculate the output voltage, V_{out}, for each temperature.

Answer

At 24°C:

$$V_{out} = \frac{R_2}{R_1 + R_2} V_{in}$$

$$\Rightarrow V_{out} = \frac{500}{500 + 300} \times 9 = 5.6 \text{ V}$$

At 60°C:

$$V_{out} = \frac{R_2}{R_1 + R_2} V_{in}$$

$$\Rightarrow V_{out} = \frac{500}{500 + 120} \times 9 = 7.3 \text{ V}$$

It can be seen that the output voltage increases with increasing temperature.

Knowledge check 32

At a certain light level, the LDR in Figure 58 has a resistance of 1.0 kΩ. Calculate the output voltage of the circuit.

Although the output will increase with increasing input, it is unlikely to be linear because the change of resistance with either temperature or light level is non-linear, and a calibration curve is likely to be needed in order to be able to relate output voltage to input.

A calibration curve can be obtained using the apparatus and circuit shown in Figure 59. R_2 is 500 Ω.

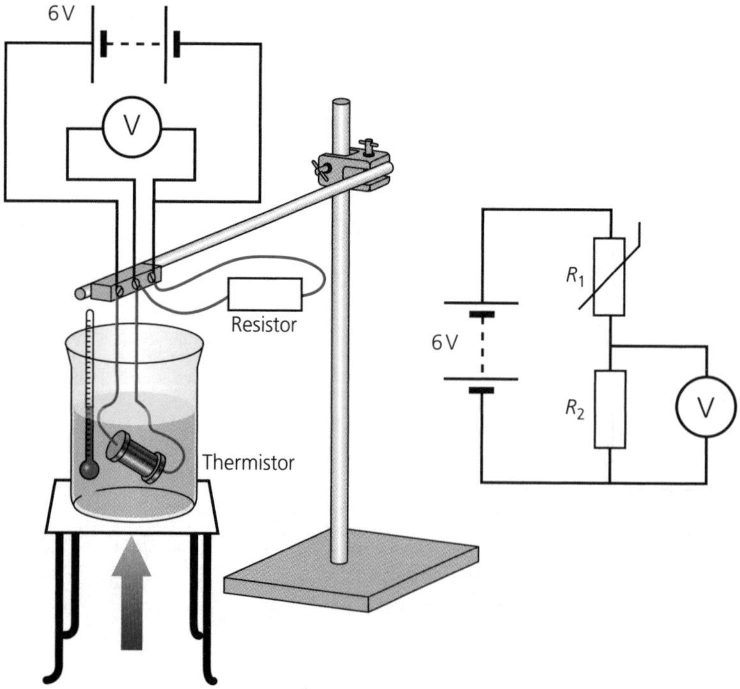

Figure 59 Measuring the calibration curve for a thermistor

Take care to keep the leads well supported and away from the source of heat. Wear safety goggles when carrying out this experiment.

A typical calibration curve for a thermistor using this arrangement might look like Figure 60.

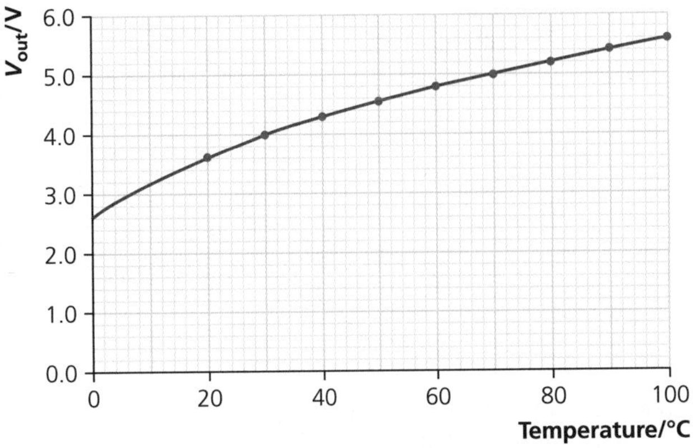

Figure 60 Typical calibration curve for a thermistor in a potential divider circuit

The output can be used with an electronic switch to turn a heating circuit on or off at a set temperature.

Summary

After studying this topic you should:

- know how to use a potential divider circuit to obtain a potential difference from an input potential difference or power supply
- understand how a potential divider circuit is used with a thermistor or a light dependent resistor to produce a changing voltage output as the input is changed

Electromotive force and internal resistance

So far we have assumed that cells have a constant potential difference across them. However, when connected in a circuit, this is not the case because every cell has an internal resistance and some energy is always lost inside them as a result.

Any cell or generator can be thought of as having two elements. One element does work on each coulomb of charge that passes through the cell. This work done per coulomb is called the **electromotive force** or **emf**. It is defined as:

$$\varepsilon = \frac{E}{Q}$$

As the unit of work is J and the unit of charge is C, emf is measured in $\mathrm{J\,C^{-1}}$ or V (volt).

However, every source of emf also includes some resistance. For a cell, this would be the chemicals in the cell. For a generator, it would be the wires of the generator and for devices like solar cells, it would be the semiconductor that makes up the cell. We call this the **internal resistance**. Although the resistance is always an integral part of the source of the emf, we generally show a cell with its internal resistance in series with the source of the emf, as shown in Figure 61.

Electromotive force (**emf**) is the total work done on each coulomb that passes through the source of the emf.

Internal resistance is the resistance that is part of the source of the emf and cannot be separated from the source.

The internal resistance is labelled r and the dashed box shows the complete cell which cannot, in fact, be separated out into the part that generates the emf, ε, and the internal resistance, r. The potential difference, V, is the potential difference measured across the terminals of the cell.

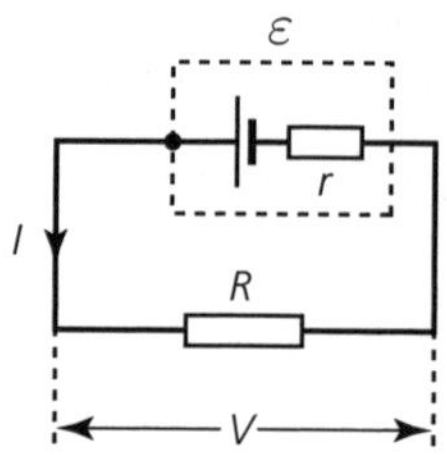

Figure 61 A cell with internal resistance connected to an external resistor, R

Applying the conservation of energy to this circuit, the emf of the cell equals the work done by each coulomb in the external resistor plus work done by each coulomb in the internal resistance:

$$\varepsilon = IR + Ir$$

This simplifies to:

$$\varepsilon = I(R + r)$$

Or, since for the external resistance $V = IR$:

$$\varepsilon = V + Ir$$

If the current is zero, then $\varepsilon = V$, so the emf of a cell can be measured approximately using a modern digital voltmeter with a very high resistance, as the current will be negligible.

Required practical 6

Investigation of the emf and internal resistance of electric cells and batteries

The emf and internal resistance of electric cells and batteries can be investigated by measuring the variation of the terminal potential difference of the cell with current in it.

Measuring the internal resistance and emf of a cell is straightforward using the circuit shown in Figure 62.

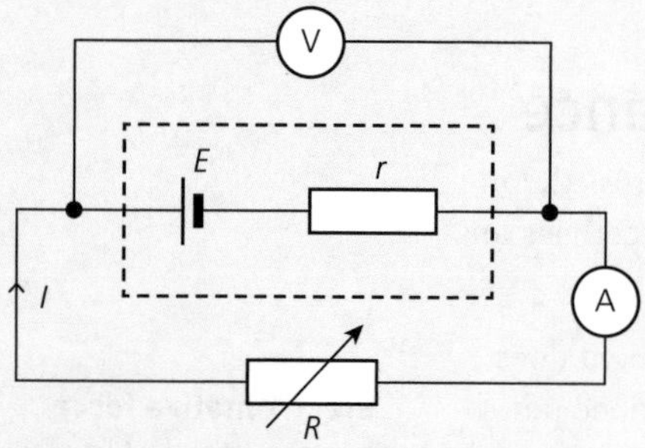

Figure 62 Circuit for measuring the internal resistance and emf of a cell

The external resistance, R, is varied and values of potential difference and current are measured. Using:

$$\varepsilon = V + Ir$$

Rearranged to give V as the subject:

$$V = -Ir + \varepsilon \text{ (or } V = -rI + \varepsilon\text{)}$$

This is in the form $y = mx + c$, so the resulting potential difference–current graph is a straight line with gradient $-r$ and an intercept on the y-axis of ε, as shown in Figure 63.

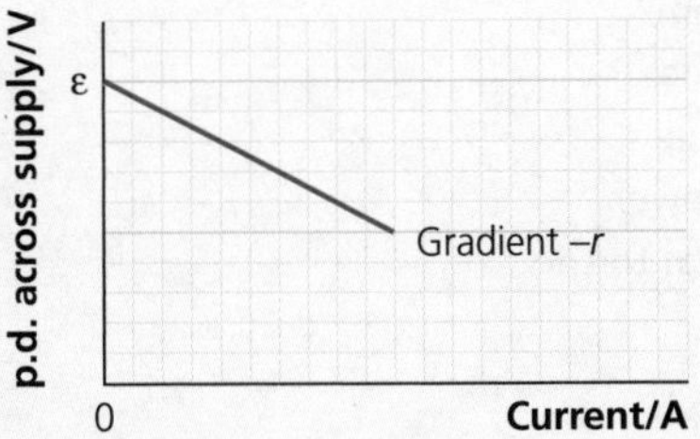

Figure 63 Graph obtained when measuring the terminal potential difference for a cell and the current through the cell

The circuit in Figure 62 is used to measure the internal resistance of a 'D' type cell. The external resistance, R, is varied and values of terminal potential difference and current are measured. The results are shown in Table 8.

Current/A	0.06	0.10	0.20	0.40	0.60	0.80	0.98
p.d./V	1.50	1.45	1.35	1.15	0.95	0.76	0.55

Table 8

From these data, draw a graph of potential difference against current and find the internal resistance of the cell and the emf. A suitable graph would be as shown in Figure 64.

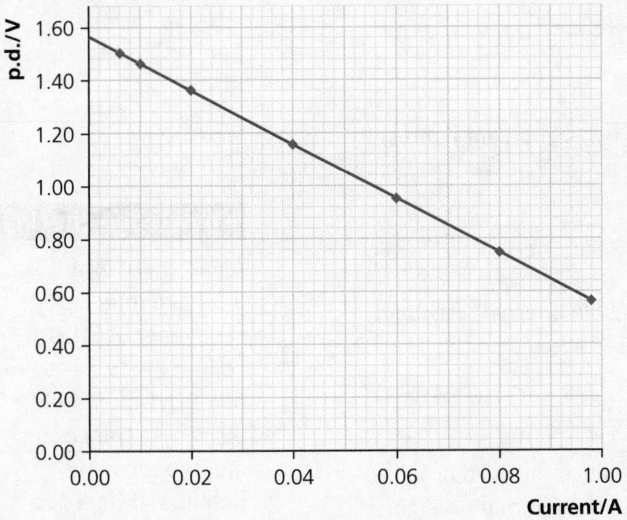

Figure 64

In this case, the gradient of the graph is:

$$-r = \frac{0.80-1.56}{0.74} = -1.03\ \Omega$$

Therefore, r is 1.0 Ω.

The intercept is 1.56 V, therefore the emf is 1.56 V.

The internal resistance of a source of emf can make a significant difference to calculations. You may be required to take the internal resistance into account unless a question specifically tells you that the cell has negligible internal resistance, in which case you can ignore its effects.

Exam tip

You should be able to describe how to measure the internal resistance and emf of a cell.

The greater the internal resistance of a cell, the lower the current available from the cell. This is because, as the current increases, the potential difference across the internal resistance increases. Since $\varepsilon = V + IR$, this means that the potential difference across the external load will also decrease. In fact, the maximum power available to the external load is when the resistance of the external load is equal to the internal resistance of the source.

This is one reason why, for example, a car battery, which has a very low internal resistance, is needed to start a car rather than a set of 'D' cells which may have the same emf but a much higher internal resistance.

Worked example

A cell of emf 1.5 V and internal resistance 0.10 Ω is connected to a lamp of resistance 0.45 Ω.

a Calculate the potential difference across the lamp.
b Calculate the current through the lamp.
c Calculate the power dissipated in the lamp.
d Calculate the power wasted in the internal resistance.

Answers

a The circuit behaves like a potential divider. Therefore:

$$V_R = \frac{R}{R+r}V$$

$$\Rightarrow V_R = \frac{0.45}{0.45+0.10} \times 1.5 = 1.23 \text{ V} \quad (1.2\text{ V to two significant figures})$$

b $$I = \frac{V}{R} = \frac{1.23}{0.45} = 2.7 \text{ A}$$

c $$P = VI = 1.23 \times 2.7 = 3.3 \text{ W}$$

It is interesting to note that if the cell had negligible internal resistance, the power would have been given by:

$$P = \frac{V^2}{R} = \frac{1.5^2}{0.45} = 5.0 \text{ W}$$

The effect of the internal resistance is both to reduce the current in the circuit and cause some power to be dissipated in the internal resistance.

d The power wasted in the internal resistance is given by:

$$P = I^2R = 2.7^2 \times 0.10 = 0.73 \text{ W}$$

Knowledge check 33

A battery of emf 3.0 V and internal resistance 2.0 Ω is connected to a resistor of 6.0 Ω. Calculate the current in the circuit and the terminal potential difference of the battery when connected in the circuit.

Summary

After studying this topic you should:

- understand the terms electromotive force (emf) and terminal potential difference
- be able to use the conservation of energy to explain the emf and terminal potential difference in a circuit
- know how to measure the internal resistance and emf of a cell or battery
- be able to make circuit calculations in situations where the internal resistance is not negligible

Questions & Answers

There are two papers for AS and three papers for A-level (the third paper for A-level assesses practical skills and the options). At AS each of the papers lasts 1 hour 30 minutes and has 70 marks allocated. One of the papers will contain some multiple-choice questions and both papers will contain a mixture of long and short answer questions.

At A-level each paper lasts 2 hours and has 85 marks allocated. Papers 1 and 2 will contain multiple-choice questions, and short and long answer questions.

You can find past papers and specimen papers at:

www.aqa.org.uk/subjects/science/as-and-a-level/physics-7407-7408

As multiple-choice questions give a chance to check knowledge and understanding over a wide range of topics, both test papers in this book contain 20 multiple-choice questions, which makes them suitable for both AS and A-level practice. In addition, for one question in each test paper there is an alternative AS question and a harder A-level question on the same material.

There is a data booklet which can be downloaded from the AQA website which contains almost all the formulae explained in this book.

Command words

There are a number of standard command words that are used by examiners and you should know exactly what each one means. There is a complete list of command words and their meanings on the AQA website, but some of the more common ones are:

Apply: use knowledge or understanding in a new situation.

Calculate: work out a value of something using given data.

Describe: give an account of something, for example an experimental procedure or a method of carrying out a process.

Determine: use available data to find an answer.

Estimate: this also means to work something out but you may have to make assumptions or gather data from a graph elsewhere in order to complete the task. If you make any assumptions, you should always state what assumptions you have made.

Explain: give reasons for something. You will sometimes find the two command words **state** and **explain** together when you are expected to state a piece of knowledge and then explain why this is so with reference to key physics.

Show (that): provide evidence to demonstrate a conclusion. This is often used when the result of a calculation is needed in a subsequent part of a question. You should always work out any answer to at least one more significant figure than the figures given in the question to show that you have actually done the calculation.

Sketch: this might be a diagram of apparatus or it may be a graph. If it is a graph, a sketch graph has axes and labels and, if available, some key data points such as a maximum value. It is less precise than plotting a graph but gives key information.

State: express a piece of knowledge or understanding clearly. Sometimes a single figure, formula or few words will be adequate for this.

Suggest: this means that you are expected to use your knowledge of physics, perhaps in a new situation, to give a reason for something. There is often no single correct answer but your reasoning is important.

About this section

You may want to try the test papers as full practice papers, or you may prefer to try individual questions and use the commentaries and answers to help you to understand how to answer such questions. Actual examination papers require you to answer on the paper but that is not possible in this book, so you may have to transfer some diagrams and graphs to your own paper.

The answers given are not necessarily model answers and other ways of doing the same calculation are sometimes possible. The answers are intended to show you how to approach a question and what gains marks in an examination.

Some questions have a brief analysis of what to watch for when answering the question (preceded by the icon ⓔ). They offer tips on what you need to do to gain full marks. Some answers are followed by comments highlighting where credit is due or could be missed (indicated by the icon ⓔ).

Note that if you are taking an AS examination in physics, the questions will not be quite as difficult as the questions you will get on the same material for A-level. The A-level questions are highlighted in the test papers.

Test paper 1

1 hour 30 minutes, 70 marks

Questions 1–20 are multiple-choice questions. For each question, select one answer from A to D.

Question 1

Which of the following is a vector quantity?

A Mass **B** Weight **C** Distance **D** Energy

Question 2

You walk 40 m due north followed by 60 m due east. Your displacement is:

A 100 m northeast **B** 72 m at 56° east **C** 72 m at 34° east **D** 50 m at 45° east

Question 3

A boy pulls a bag along by pulling at 50° to the horizontal with a force of 70 N. The horizontal component of the force is:

A 54 N **B** 83 N **C** 45 N **D** 17 N

Question 4

A car of mass 1.0×10^3 kg is on a hill that slopes at 20° to the horizontal. The component of the weight of the car acting down the hill is:

A 3.4×10^3 N **B** 9.2×10^3 N **C** 340 N **D** 920 N

Question 5

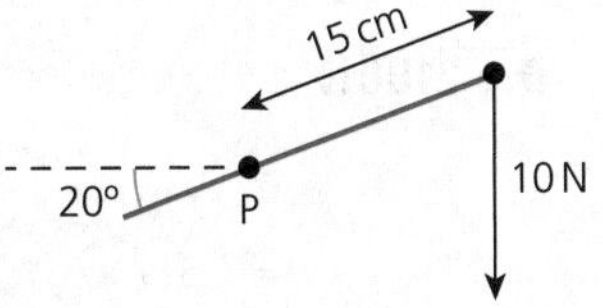

Figure 1

A lever is being pulled down with a force of 10 N about a pivot, P, as shown in Figure 1. The moment of the 10 N force is:

A 0.51 N m **B** 1.41 N m **C** 1.5 N m **D** 150 N m

Question 6

A door is 70 cm wide. A force of 50 N is applied perpendicular to the door at the opposite edge to the hinge to open the door. The force that needs to be applied on the other side, 30 cm from the hinge, in order to stop the door opening is:

A 15 N **B** 21 N **C** 100 N **D** 120 N

Question 7

A 1 m ruler is balanced about the 30 cm mark by a mass of 300 g hung at the 10 cm mark. The mass of the ruler is:

A 0.30 kg **B** 0.45 kg **C** 0.17 kg **D** 0.60 kg

Question 8

A skydiver of mass 65 kg is in freefall. The drag from air resistance is 150 N. The skydiver's acceleration is:

A 2.3 m s^{-2} **B** 7.5 m s^{-2} **C** 9.8 m s^{-2} **D** 12 m s^{-2}

Question 9

A skydiver reaches a terminal velocity of 50 m s^{-1}. At this time:

A There are no forces acting on the skydiver.

B A Newton's law pair of forces of the skydiver's weight and the air resistance are equal.

C The resultant of the forces acting on the skydiver is zero.

D There is no gravitational force at that height.

Question 10

A fairground ride brings a passenger to rest from a speed of 30 m s^{-1} in 1.5 s. The passenger has a mass of 70 kg. The force required to do this was:

A 690 N **B** 1000 N **C** 1400 N **D** 2100 N

Question 11

A space rocket is a long way from Earth. It fires its engines to accelerate. In this situation, a pair of forces that are described by Newton's third law are:

A Gravity and the thrust of the rocket

B The force of the gases from the rocket engine and gravity

C The gases pushing on the rocket and the drag on the rocket

D The rocket pushing on the expelled gases and the expelled gases pushing on the rocket

In Questions 12 and 13, which of the velocity–time graphs shown in Figure 2 best represents the situation described? Each graph may be used once, more than once or not at all.

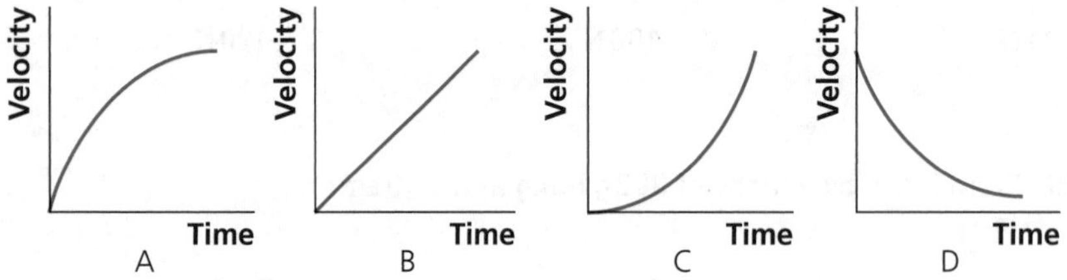

Figure 2

Question 12

A small steel sphere is released from an electromagnet and is falling freely:

A Graph A **B** Graph B **C** Graph C **D** Graph D

Question 13

A skydiver as he jumps from a plane:

A Graph A **B** Graph B **C** Graph C **D** Graph D

Question 14

A ball is thrown horizontally at 5.0 m s^{-1} and hits the ground after 0.64 s. The height from which it was thrown is:

A 7.8 m **B** 5.2 m **C** 3.2 m **D** 2.0 m

Question 15

A tennis ball of mass 60 g is thrown at a wall at 15 m s^{-1}. It rebounds at the same speed. Its change of momentum is:

A 0.90 kg m s^{-1} **B** 1.8 kg m s^{-1} **C** 900 kg m s^{-1} **D** 1800 kg m s^{-1}

Question 16

The unit for work done is:

A N m^{-1} **B** N m^{-2} **C** N m **D** N m^{2}

Question 17

The power drawn by a train travelling at 30 m s^{-1} with a resistive force of 80 kN is:

A 2.4 kW **B** 2.7 kW **C** 2.4 MW **D** 72 MW

Question 18

Figure 3 shows the force–extension curve for a wire.

The limit of proportionality is most likely to be at point:

A P **B** Q

C R **D** S

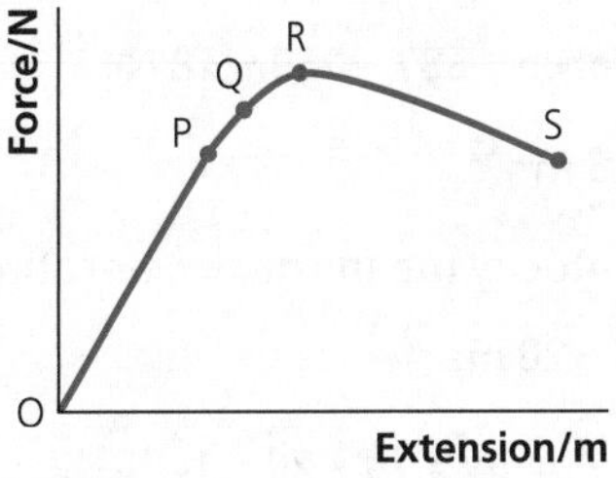

Figure 3

Question 19

The best unit for tensile stress is:

A N m **B** N m^{2} **C** No unit **D** Pa

Question 20

Figure 4 shows the stress–strain curves for two materials.

Which of the following statements is correct?

A Material A is stiffer than material B but not as strong.

B Material A is less stiff than material B but stronger.

C Material A is stiffer and stronger than material B.

D Material A is less stiff than material B and not as strong.

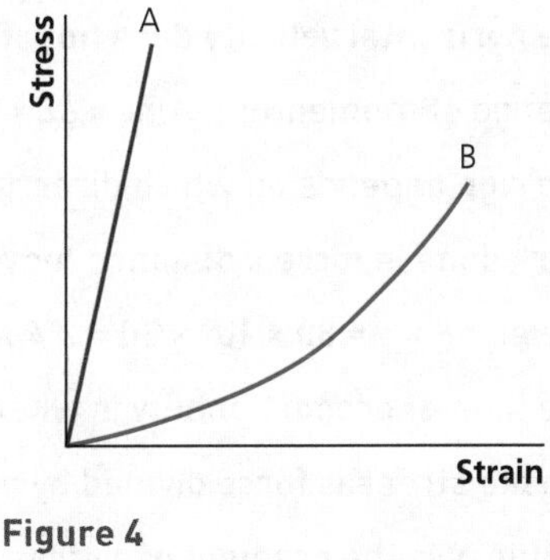

Figure 4

(Total 20 marks)

Answers to questions 1–20

1 B Weight acts downwards towards the centre of the Earth so has direction.

2 B Use Pythagoras' theorem to calculate the resultant:

$\sqrt{40^2+60^2}$

The angle is then given by:

$\tan^{-1}\left(\frac{60}{40}\right)=56°$

3 C horizontal force = 70 cos 50° = 45 N

4 A force down the hill = 1000 × 9.8 × sin 20° = 3.4×10^3 N

5 B moment = $F \times d \sin\theta$ (see Figure 10) = 10 × 0.15 × sin 70° = 1.41 N m

6 D Using the principle of moments:

0.70 × 50 = F × 0.30 m

Therefore F = 117 N, or 120 N to two significant figures.

7 A The centre of mass of the ruler is at 50 cm. Taking moments:

0.20 × 0.30 × 9.8 = 0.20 × M × 9.8

Therefore, M = 0.30 kg.

8 B weight = 65 × 9.8 = 637 N

resultant force = 637 − 150 = 487 N

$a=\frac{487}{65}=7.5\ \text{m s}^{-2}$

9 C Terminal velocity means no acceleration, therefore no resultant force.

10 C $a=\frac{\Delta v}{\Delta t}=\frac{30}{1.5}=20\ \text{ms}^{-2}$

Therefore, $F = ma$ = 70 × 20 = 1400 N.

11 D Newton's third law states that forces must be equal, opposite and of the same type.

12 B If acceleration is constant, the gradient of a velocity–time graph is constant.

13 A A skydiver will start accelerating, but as speed increases so does air resistance, so acceleration decreases until the skydiver eventually reaches terminal velocity.

14 D The horizontal velocity does not affect the vertical motion. Use $s = \frac{1}{2}gt^2$.

15 B Change of momentum: $\Delta mv = 60 \times 10^{-3} \times (-15-15) = -1.8\ \text{kg m s}^{-1}$

The sign depends on which direction is taken as positive.

16 C Work done is force × distance moved in the direction of the force.

17 C power = $F \times v$ = 80 × 10^3 × 30 = 2.4×10^6 W

18 A The limit of proportionality is where the graph stops being linear.

19 D Tensile stress is force divided by area with the unit N m^{-2} or Pa.

20 C Stiffness is the gradient of a stress–strain graph and strength is the breaking stress. Material A has a steeper gradient and the breaking stress is higher than for material B.

Question 21

Figure 5 shows a car moving along a level road at a constant velocity.

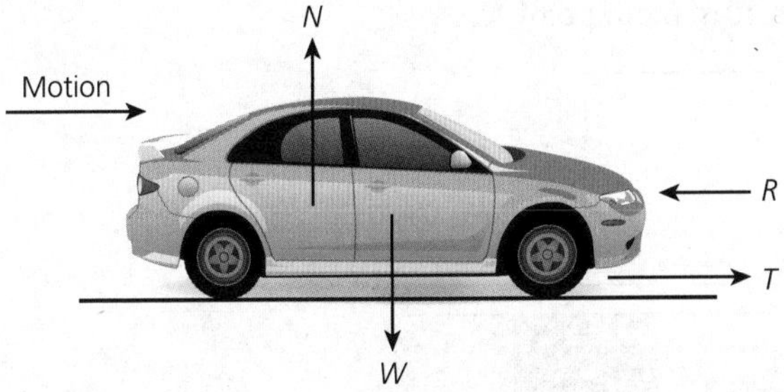

Figure 5

(a) State Newton's third law of motion. (2 marks)

(b) Force *W* is the weight of the car. State what is the Newton's third law opposing force to the car's weight. (2 marks)

(c) State and explain which forces must be equal in magnitude. (4 marks)

(Total 8 marks)

ⓔ This question is testing your knowledge of Newton's laws and your ability to apply these laws. Parts (a) and (b) require you to recall Newton's third law and how it applies to forces. Part (c) requires you to apply your understanding of forces and motion.

Answers

(a) If body A exerts a force on body B, then body B will exert an equal ✓ and opposite force on body A of the same type ✓.

(b) The Newton's third law opposing force to the weight of the car is the force that is exerted by the car ✓ upwards by the Earth ✓.

(c) Since the car is moving at a constant velocity, the forward force, *T*, must be equal and opposite to the resistive force, *R*, ✓ so that the resultant horizontal force is zero ✓.

The car is not moving vertically so the normal reaction, *N*, must be equal and opposite to the weight, *W*, ✓ so that the resultant vertical force is zero ✓.

Question 22

Figure 6 shows two cars driving across a bridge, 30 m apart. The cars have a mass of 1500 kg each. At the time shown, the leading car is 10 m from point A.

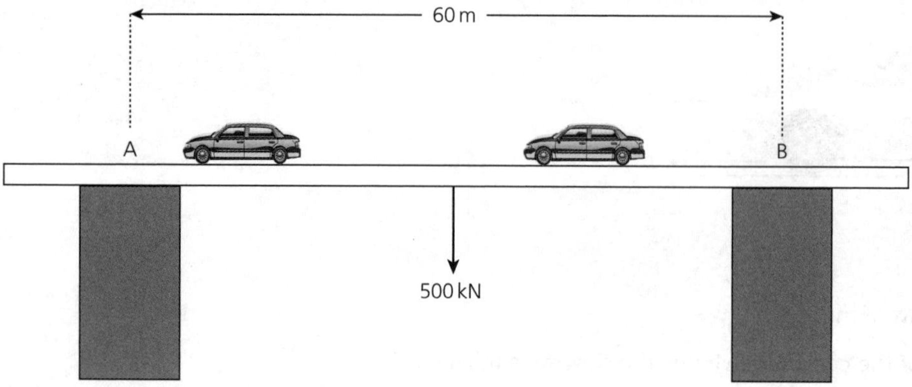

Figure 6

Assume $g = 9.8\,\text{N kg}^{-1}$.

(a) **Calculate the total downward force on the two bridge supports.** (2 marks)

(b) **Calculate the forces exerted on the roadway by each of the bridge supports at point A and point B.** (4 marks)

(c) **Describe what happens to the forces exerted by the bridge supports as the cars continue across the bridge until the leading car reaches point A.** (2 marks)

(Total 8 marks)

ⓔ This question tests your ability to use moments to calculate forces. Make sure you show all your working.

Answers

(a) total downward force = $(1500 \times 9.8 \times 2) + (500 \times 10^3)$ ✓ = 5.3×10^5 N = 530 kN ✓

(b) Taking moments about A:

clockwise moments = $(14700 \times 10) + (14700 \times 40) + (500000 \times 30) = 1.57 \times 10^7$ Nm ✓

anticlockwise moment = $F_B \times 60$ ✓

$F_B \times 60 = 1.57 \times 10^6$ Nm

$F_B = 260$ kN ✓

$F_A = 530 - 260 = 270$ kN ✓

(c) The force exerted by the bridge support at point A increases ✓ as the force exerted by the bridge support at point B decreases ✓.

Question 23 (AS question)

A ball is thrown horizontally from a height of 5.0 m at a velocity of 4.0 m s^{-1}.

(a) Describe the path of the ball after it is thrown. Assume air resistance is negligible. (3 marks)

(b) Calculate the time taken for the ball to reach the ground. (2 marks)

(c) Show that the horizontal distance from where the ball was thrown to where it lands is 4.0 m. (1 mark)

(d) Explain the difference that might be observed in the path of the ball if the ball was:

(i) The same mass but much larger (1 mark)

(ii) The same size but four times the mass (1 mark)

(Total 8 marks)

ⓔ This question is testing your understanding of projectile motion and the concept that horizontal and vertical motion can be treated separately. Part (d) requires you to apply your understanding of air resistance to explain changes in motion.

Answers

(a) The path is a parabola ✓ in which the vertical motion is accelerating ✓ and the horizontal motion is a constant velocity ✓.

(b) Use $s = ut + \frac{1}{2}at^2$ for the vertical motion ✓. Substituting $s = 5.0$ m and $u = 0$ m s^{-1}:

$$t = \sqrt{\frac{2s}{g}} = \sqrt{\frac{2 \times 5.0}{9.8}} = 1.0 \text{ s}$$ ✓

(c) In 1 s, the ball will travel $4.0 \times 1.0 = 4.0$ m ✓.

(d) (i) If the ball is much larger, the air resistance will be greater which might cause the ball to take a little more time to fall. However, this will probably not compensate for the slowing in the horizontal direction caused by air resistance, so it will probably land at a distance less than 4.0 m ✓.

ⓔ Here the mark will be for your correct understanding of the possible effects of increased air resistance. You might say it lands in the same place or not, as long as you explain your reasons.

Answers

(d) (ii) Neither the horizontal nor the vertical motion should be affected by the increased mass. Air resistance will have less of an effect on the motion so the path will be more parabolic ✓.

ⓔ Again, the mark will be for showing your understanding of the effect of less significant air resistance on motion.

Question 23 (A-level question)

A ball is thrown upwards from a height of 2.0 m with a velocity of 5.0 m s^{-1} at an angle of 30° to the horizontal. Assume air resistance is negligible.

(a) Calculate the initial horizontal and vertical velocities. (2 marks)

(b) Calculate the time taken for the ball to reach the ground. (3 marks)

(c) Show that the ball hits the ground about 4.0 m from where it was thrown. (1 mark)

In fact, there is air resistance.

(d) Explain how the air resistance will affect the path of the ball. (2 marks)

(Total 8 marks)

ⓔ This question is testing your ability to carry out more complex calculations on projectile motion. Part (a) requires you to find the components of a vector. Part (d) asks you to demonstrate your understanding of the effect of air resistance on the path of the ball.

Answers

(a) horizontal velocity = $v \times \cos\theta = 5.0 \times \cos 30° = 4.3$ m s^{-1} ✓

vertical velocity = $v \times \sin\theta = 5.0 \times \sin 30° = 2.5$ m s^{-1} ✓

(b) Use the equation $s = ut + \frac{1}{2}gt^2$, but $u = -2.5$ m s^{-1} (upwards) ✓, therefore:

$2.0 = -2.5t + \frac{1}{2} \times 9.8t^2$

Rearranging:

$4.9t^2 - 2.5t - 2 = 0$ ✓

Now use the equation for solving quadratic equations which gives:

$t = 0.94$ s (or 0.43 s) ✓

(c) horizontal distance = horizontal velocity × time = 4.3 × 0.94 = 4.0 m ✓

(d) Air resistance will cause the path to be less parabolic ✓. The ball will not go as high or as far horizontally ✓.

Question 24

A hammer is used to hit a nail. Just as the hammer hits the nail, it is travelling at 20 m s^{-1}. It is brought to rest in 0.10 s.

(a) Show that the acceleration of the hammer is about 200 m s^{-2}. (2 marks)

(b) The hammer has a mass of 150 g. Calculate the average force exerted by the nail on the hammer. (1 mark)

(c) The nail does not move when it is hit. Explain, using all three of Newton's laws, why the nail may not have moved. (3 marks)

(Total 6 marks)

ⓔ This question requires you to be able to apply equations of motion to a situation and to understand how all three of Newton's laws apply to the hammer and nail. In particular, you should be able to show that you know the forces in Newton's third law are of the same type.

Answers

(a) $a = \Delta v / \Delta t$ ✓ $= 200\,\text{m}\,\text{s}^{-2}$ ✓

(b) $F = m \times a = 0.15 \times 200 = 30\,\text{N}$ ✓

(c) If the nail does not move, then from Newton's first law there must be no resultant force acting on it ✓.

Newton's second law allows us to calculate the force on the hammer and according to Newton's third law, there is an equal and opposite force of 30 N exerted by the hammer on the nail ✓.

Since there is no resultant force, there must be a frictional force of 30 N on the nail from the surrounding material and, therefore, the nail must also exert an equal and opposite frictional force of 30 N on the surrounding material ✓.

Question 25

A trolley of mass 0.80 kg is placed on a slope at an angle of 30° to the horizontal. Assume friction is negligible.

(a) Show that the force down the slope is about 4 N. (2 marks)

(b) Calculate the acceleration of the trolley down the slope. (1 mark)

Friction is not negligible and the velocity of the trolley is found to increase from rest to 11.4 m s^{-1} in 3 s.

(c) Calculate the frictional force up the slope. (3 marks)

(Total 6 marks)

ⓔ In this question, you need to be able to find the components of a force and in part (b) use the components of force to find an acceleration. Part (a) is a 'show that' question, so your answer must be to at least one more significant figure than the value given in the question. If you cannot work out the answer to part (a), you can use the value given to work out part (b). However, if you have calculated a value in part (a), you should use your calculated value in the next part of the question. In part (c), you are tested on your understanding of resultant forces.

Answers

(a) Force is the component of the weight of the trolley acting down the slope ✓:

$0.80 \times 9.8 \times \sin 30 = 3.9\,\text{N}$ ✓

(b) $a = \frac{F}{m} = \frac{3.9}{0.80} = 4.9 ms^{-2}$ ✓

(c) Use $v = u + at$ to find $a = 3.8\,\text{m}\,\text{s}^{-2}$ ✓. Then: $F = m \times a = 0.80 \times 3.8 = 3.0\,\text{N}$ ✓

Therefore, the frictional force must be $3.9 - 3.0 = 0.9\,\text{N}$ up the slope ✓.

Question 26

A student sets up an experiment to measure the Young modulus of a piece of copper wire, using the apparatus shown in Figure 7.

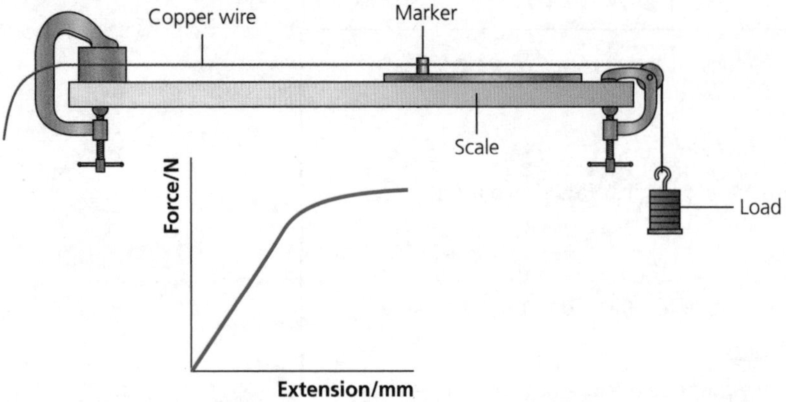

Figure 7

A piece of wire 2.00 m long is used and forces of 0–10 N are applied to the wire. The results are analysed using a stress–strain graph as shown in Figure 8.

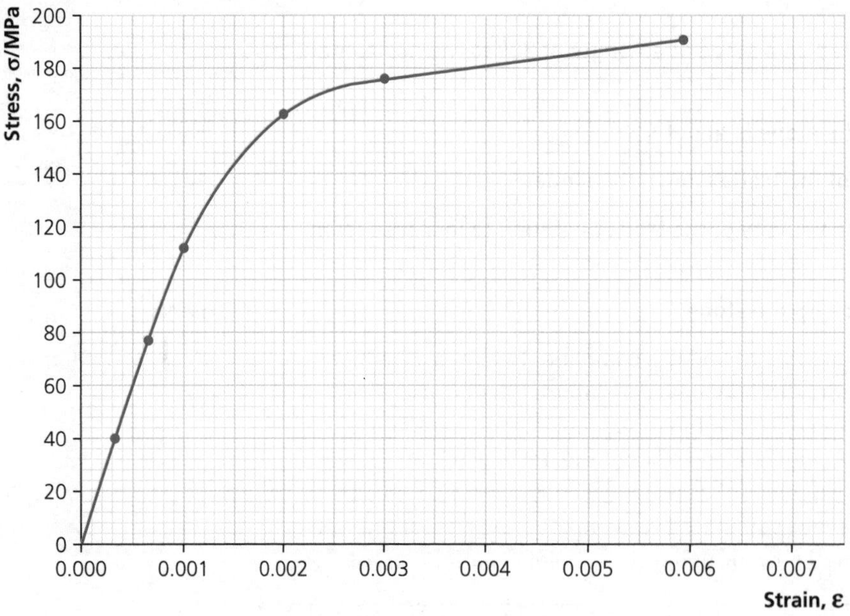

Figure 8

(a) **Define the terms tensile stress and tensile strain.** (2 marks)

The diameter of the wire is measured with a micrometer in several places and the average value is calculated to be 0.26 mm.

(b) **Explain why the diameter is measured in several places.** (1 mark)

(c) **Show that this diameter gives a cross-sectional area of 5.3×10^{-8} m^2.** (1 mark)

(d) **Calculate the stress in the wire when the applied force is 4.1 N.** (1 mark)

(e) Use the graph to estimate a value for the Young modulus of copper. (2 marks)

(f) Explain where you think the greatest uncertainties will be in this experiment. (2 marks)

(Total 9 marks)

e This question tests your knowledge of experimental technique and your ability to analyse data. You should have done an experiment similar to this and therefore be familiar with the type of measurements and analysis required.

Answers

(a) tensile stress $= \dfrac{\text{force}}{\text{cross–sectional area}}$ ✓

tensile strain $= \dfrac{\text{extension}}{\text{original length}}$ ✓

(b) The diameter is measured in several places as the wire may not be uniform or exactly round in cross-section. By measuring in several places, an average value can be obtained as well as an indication of the uncertainty ✓.

(c) $A = \pi r^2 = \pi \times \left(\dfrac{0.26 \times 10^{-3}}{2}\right)^2 = 5.31 \times 10^{-8}\,\text{m}^2$

(5.3×10^{-8} to two significant figures) ✓

e As part (c) is a 'show that' question, give your answer to one more significant figure than the value given in the question.

Answers

(d) stress $= \dfrac{F}{A} = \dfrac{4.1}{5.31 \times 10^{-8}} = 7.7 \times 10^{7}\,\text{Pa} = 77\,\text{MPa}$

(e) The Young modulus is equal to the gradient of the straight part of the line ✓:

$\dfrac{200 \times 10^{6}}{0.0017} = 1.18 \times 10^{11}\,\text{Pa}$ ✓

e In part (e), you could use a ruler to extend the initial straight part of the line in order to make calculating the gradient easier. In an examination question, draw on the graph given to show how you obtained your values.

Answer

(f) The two sources of greatest uncertainty are in measuring the diameter of the wire ✓ and the extension ✓.

The uncertainty in the measurement of the diameter of the wire is likely to be about ±5%, which means an uncertainty of ±10% in the cross-sectional area.

From the data, the initial extension is about 1–2 mm and by measuring with a metre rule, the uncertainty in this is very large.

e In part (f), you should be able to identify at least one uncertainty in experimental data and explain why the uncertainty arises.

Question 27

A car accelerates from rest to 10 m s^{-1}. The mass of the car is 1500 kg and 225 kJ of chemical energy from the fuel is used during the acceleration.

(a) **Calculate the final kinetic energy of the car.** (1 mark)

(b) **Calculate the efficiency of the car's engine.** (1 mark)

The car is now brought to rest using the brakes.

(c) **State what has happened to the kinetic energy of the car.** (1 mark)

(d) **Explain how energy conservation systems can be incorporated into the design of transport systems.** (2 marks)

(Total 5 marks)

ⓔ This question is testing your understanding of energy transfer and whether you can apply principles of conservation of energy to specific problems.

Answers

(a) kinetic energy $= \frac{1}{2}mv^2 = \frac{1}{2} \times 1500 \times 10^2 = 7.5 \times 10^4 = 75$ kJ ✓

(b) efficiency $= \frac{\text{useful energy output}}{\text{total energy input}} \times 100\% = \frac{75\,000}{225\,000} \times 100\% = 33\%$ ✓

(c) Kinetic energy is transferred as heat to the surroundings ✓.

ⓔ In part (c), simply writing 'heat' is not enough, you need to explain where the heat goes.

Answer

(d) (A lot of energy is wasted when braking.) Some of this energy can be recovered and stored as gravitational potential energy ✓ as in the case of trains. In the case of buses, the energy can be stored as kinetic energy of a rotating flywheel, and in the case of car batteries, it can be stored as chemical energy ✓.

ⓔ In part (d), you would not have to write about all methods of recovering kinetic energy in transport systems, but you should be able to explain at least one method.

(Total for test paper 1: 70 marks)

Test paper 2

1 hour 30 minutes, 70 marks

Questions 1–20 are multiple-choice questions. For each question, select one answer from A to D.

Questions 1–3

Here is a list of electrical units. For questions 1–3, choose the correct unit for the quantity given:

A As **B** Cs^{-1} **C** JC^{-1} **D** VA^{-1}

1 Potential difference

2 Electric current

3 Resistance

Questions 4 and 5 refer to the resistor network shown in Figure 1.

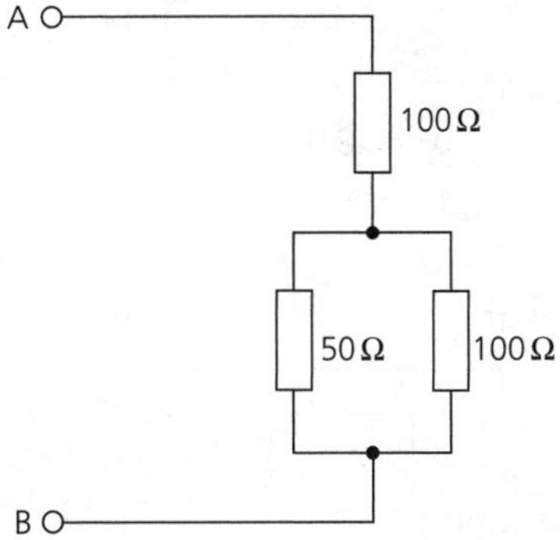

Figure 1

Question 4

The resistance between A and B is:

A 300 Ω **B** 200 Ω **C** 150 Ω **D** 133 Ω

Question 5

A potential difference of 6.0 V is applied across A and B. The current in the 50 Ω resistor is:

A 0.03 A **B** 0.015 A **C** 0.045 A **D** 0.12 A

Question 6

A beam of ions delivers a charge of 80 nC in a time of 40 s. The current carried by the beam is:

A 2.0 A **B** 2.0×10^{-3} A **C** 2.0×10^{-6} A **D** 2.0×10^{-9} A

Question 7

A resistor of value *R* has a potential difference, *V*, across it. The potential difference is then halved. The power dissipated in the resistor will be changed by a factor of:

A ×2 **B** $\times\frac{1}{2}$ **C** ×4 **D** $\times\frac{1}{4}$

Question 8

The characteristic of a component is shown in Figure 2.

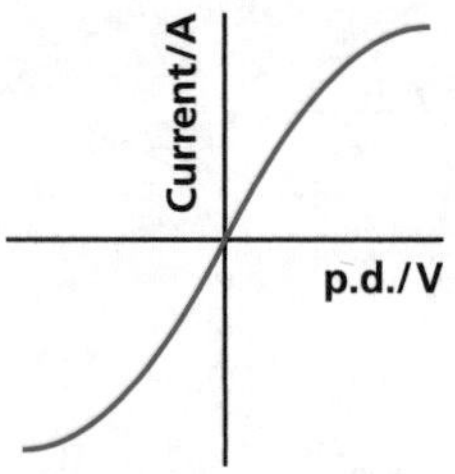

Figure 2

The component most likely to have this characteristic is:

A a diode **B** a thermistor **C** a filament lamp **D** a resistor

Question 9

The resistivity of copper is $1.7 \times 10^{-8}\,\Omega\,m$. A copper wire of length 2.0 m and cross-sectional area $4.0 \times 10^{-8}\,m^2$ has a resistance of:

A 0.43 Ω **B** 0.85 Ω **C** 1.2 Ω **D** 4.8 Ω

Question 10

The resistance of a negative temperature coefficient (NTC) thermistor decreases with increasing temperature. This is because:

A At higher temperatures, the charge carriers become more mobile.

B At higher temperatures, the charge carriers interact more with the lattice atoms.

C At higher temperatures, there are more charge carriers available to conduct.

D At higher temperatures, the lattice atoms vibrate more.

Question 11

A light dependent resistor (LDR) is put into the circuit shown in Figure 3.

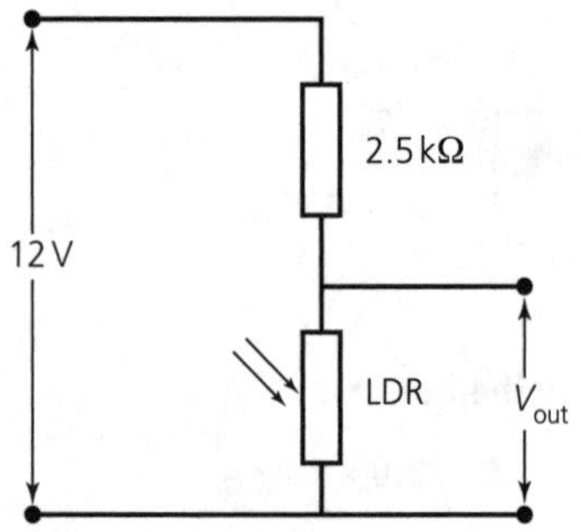

Figure 3

The value of V_{out} will:

A Increase with increasing light level.

B Decrease with increasing light level.

C Decrease with decreasing light level.

D Increase with decreasing light level.

Question 12

A cell of emf 2.0 V and internal resistance 0.50 Ω has a resistor of 5.0 Ω across its terminals. The potential difference across the 5.0 Ω resistor is:

A 0.2 V **B** 1.0 V **C** 1.8 V **D** 2.0 V

Question 13

A mains cable has a resistance of 0.5 Ω and carries a current of 4.0 A. The power dissipated in the cable is:

A 1.0 W **B** 2.0 W **C** 4.0 W **D** 8.0 W

Question 14

An electric mains shower has a working voltage of 230 V and draws a current of 15 A when operating. The energy transferred during a 10 minute shower is:

A 124 MJ **B** 2.1 MJ **C** 35 kJ **D** 3.5 kJ

Question 15

An electric lift motor raises a lift and passengers through 10 m in 5.0 s. The mass of the lift and passengers is 500 kg. The motor operates with a power of 12 kW. The efficiency of the system is:

A 82% **B** 18% **C** 24% **D** 12%

Question 16

The charge on an electron is 1.6×10^{-19} C. An electron beam carries a current of 0.20 mA. The number of electrons carried by the beam per second is:

A 1.25×10^{18} **B** 1.25×10^{15} **C** 3.2×10^{23} **D** 8.0×10^{16}

Question 17

A train requires an input electrical power of 12 MW. The potential difference for overhead power lines is 25 kV. The current drawn by the train is:

A 240 A **B** 480 A **C** 2080 A **D** 480000 A

Question 18

A circuit with two similar lamps in parallel is set up as shown in Figure 4.

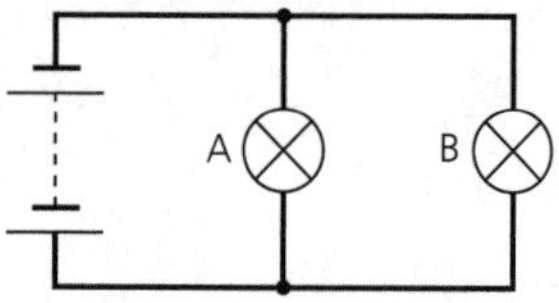

Figure 4

Which of the following statements about the potential difference across or current through the lamps is true?

A The current through A is less than through B.

B The current through A is more than through B.

C The potential difference across A is more than across B.

D The potential difference across A is the same as across B.

Question 19

A cell of emf 1.5 V and internal resistance 0.60 Ω has its terminals shorted out. The maximum current that flows is:

A 0 A **B** 0.90 A **C** 2.5 A **D** It is not possible to tell.

Question 20

A battery consists of four cells connected in series each of emf 1.5 V and internal resistance 0.60 Ω. It is connected to a resistor of value 10 Ω. The current that flows in the 10 Ω resistor is:

A 0.14 A **B** 0.48 A **C** 0.56 A **D** 0.60 A

(Total 20 marks)

Answers to questions 1–20

1 C Potential difference is work done per unit charge, $J C^{-1}$.

2 B Current is charge flowing per second, $C s^{-1}$.

3 D Resistance is potential difference divided by current, $V A^{-1}$.

4 D Calculate the resistance of the parallel part of the circuit first:

$$\frac{1}{R_{total}} = \frac{1}{100} + \frac{1}{50} = \frac{3}{100} \Rightarrow R_{total} = \frac{100}{3} = 33\ \Omega$$

Add this in series to the 100 Ω resistor to give 133 Ω.

5 A The potential difference across the parallel combination is:

$$V = \frac{33}{133} \times 6 = 1.49\ V$$

The current through the 50 Ω resistor is:

$$\frac{1.49}{50} = 0.030 \text{ A}$$

6 D The most common error in this sort of question is forgetting the prefixes or getting them wrong. Nano (n) means × 10^{-9}, therefore the current is:

$$\frac{80 \times 10^{-9}}{40} = 2.0 \times 10^{-9} \text{A}$$

7 D Power is V^2 divided by R, therefore if V is halved, the power is now:

$$\frac{V^2}{4R} = \frac{1}{4}P$$

8 C See Figure 42 and explanation.

9 B $R = \frac{\rho l}{A} = \frac{1.7 \times 10^{-8} \times 2.0}{4.0 \times 10^{-8}} = 0.85\ \Omega$

The common error is to swap l and A.

10 C A thermistor decreases its resistance because more mobile charge carriers are released at higher temperatures. Although answers B and D are true, they do not explain the decreasing resistance.

11 B The resistance of an LDR decreases with increasing light level, therefore its proportion of total resistance decreases and the potential difference across it decreases.

12 C This is a potential divider question so:

$$V_{out} = \frac{5.0}{(5.0 + 0.50)} \times 2.0 = 1.8 \text{ V}$$

13 D power = $I^2 \times R = 4.0^2 \times 0.5 = 8.0$ W

14 B electrical energy = $V \times I \times t = 230 \times 15 \times 10 \times 60 = 2.07 \times 10^6$ J

The most common error is to forget that time must be in seconds, so 10 minutes equals 600 s.

15 A The mechanical power is:

$$\frac{mgh}{\Delta t} = \frac{500 \times 9.8 \times 10}{5.0} = 9.8 \times 10^3 \text{ W}$$

$$\text{efficiency} = \frac{9.8 \times 10^3}{12 \times 10^3} \times 100\% = 82\%$$

16 B Current is ΔQ divided by Δt, therefore the number of electrons per second is:

$$\frac{I}{e} = \frac{0.20 \times 10^{-3}}{1.6 \times 10^{-19}} = 1.25 \times 10^{15} \text{s}^{-1}$$

17 B $P = IV \Rightarrow I = \frac{P}{V} = \frac{12 \times 10^6}{25 \times 10^3} = 480 \text{ A}$

18 D This question requires you to understand that in a parallel circuit, the potential difference across components is always the same and the current is shared between the components. In this case, the current through the two lamps would be the same.

19 C As there is zero external resistance, the current is determined by the internal resistance only:

$$I = \frac{emf}{r} = \frac{1.5}{0.60} = 2.5\text{ A}$$

There will be a lot of energy dissipated in the internal resistance causing it to heat up and this could cause the cell to rupture or even catch fire.

20 B For cells in series, the emfs add together and the internal resistances add together, which makes the emf of the battery 6.0 V and the internal resistance 2.4 Ω. To work out current:

$$I = \frac{emf}{(R+r)} = \frac{6.0}{12.4} = 0.48\text{ A}$$

Question 21

A 2.2 kΩ resistor has a maximum power rating of 0.25 W.

(a) Calculate the maximum current that can be safely passed through the resistor. (1 mark)

(b) Calculate the maximum potential difference that can be applied to the resistor if it is not to burn out. (1 mark)

(Total 2 marks)

ⓔ This question requires the use of basic equations for Ohm's law and power. Do not forget to write down the equations you are going to use.

Answers

(a) $P = I^2R \Rightarrow I = \sqrt{\frac{P}{R}}$

$$= \sqrt{\frac{0.25}{2.2\times10^3}} = 0.011\text{A} ✓$$

(b) $V = IR = 0.011\times2.2\times10^3 = 24\text{ V}$ ✓

Question 22

A mystery component is tested by applying a potential difference across it and measuring the current through it. Table 1 shows the results obtained.

p.d./V	5.0	4.0	3.0	2.0	1.0	0.0	-1.0	-2.0	-3.0	-4.0	-5.0
Current/A	0.07	0.05	0.035	0.02	0.01	0	-0.01	-0.02	-0.035	-0.05	-0.07

Table 1

By making suitable calculations of resistance or otherwise, suggest what component this might be, giving your reasons. (4 marks)

(Total 4 marks)

ⓔ This question is testing your basic application of the resistance formula and, more specifically, whether you can recognise the characteristics of a component from the changes in potential difference and current. You do not have to calculate resistance, you could sketch a graph of current against potential difference and recognise the component from that. However, you must use the data given in some way in order to obtain full marks.

Answer

Resistance calculations are as follows ✓:

p.d./V	5.0	4.0	3.0	2.0	1.0	0.0	-1.0	-2.0	-3.0	-4.0	-5.0
Current/A	0.07	0.05	0.035	0.02	0.01	0	-0.01	-0.02	-0.035	-0.05	-0.07
Resistance/Ω	71	80	86	100	100		100	100	86	80	71

Thus, the resistance decreases with increasing current ✓.

The most likely component is a thermistor ✓, as increasing the current will cause the component to warm up slightly which reduces the resistance ✓.

Question 23

A 60 W electric water pump is able to pump 50 kg of water to the top of a 5.0 m high house in 2.0 minutes.

(a) Calculate the work done to raise the water to the top of the house. (1 mark)

(b) Determine the mechanical power required to raise the 50 kg of water. (1 mark)

(c) Estimate the efficiency of the electric pump. (2 marks)

(Total 4 marks)

ⓔ In this question, you are being tested on your knowledge of power, both electrical and mechanical, and its application to efficiency.

Answers

(a) work done = $m \times g \times h = 50 \times 9.8 \times 5.0 = 2.5 \times 10^3$ J ✓

(b) power = $\frac{\text{work done}}{\text{time taken}} = \frac{2.5\times10^3}{2.0\times60} = 21$ W ✓

(c) efficiency = $\frac{\text{useful power}}{\text{total power}}\times100\%$ ✓ $= \frac{21}{60}\times100\% = 35\%$ ✓

Question 24

The rear windscreen heater of a car consists of 20 identical wires connected in parallel. The power must be about 180 W for it to be effective and it is connected to the 12 V supply for the car.

(a) Calculate the total resistance of the heater. (1 mark)

(b) Calculate the resistance of one of the wires. (1 mark)

Each of the wires is 1.2 m long and is made of a material of resistivity $1.1 \times 10^{-6}\,\Omega\,m$.

(c) Show that the cross-sectional area of each wire is about $8 \times 10^{-8}\,m^2$. (1 mark)

(d) Suggest whether the wires will be visible to the driver. (2 marks)

(Total 5 marks)

e This question is using the equations of power and resistors in parallel. You are also asked to 'show that', so you must give your answer to at least one more significant figure than the value given in the question. Part (d) asks you to 'suggest' an answer. Use any data that are available for your answer, in this case you can calculate the diameter of the wires. As long as your conclusion is based on the data, it does not matter what you decide as long as you justify your answer.

Answers

(a) $P = \frac{V^2}{R}$

$\Rightarrow R = \frac{V^2}{P} = \frac{144}{180} = 0.80\,\Omega$ ✓

(b) When identical resistors are in parallel, the total resistance is given by:

$R_{total} = \frac{R}{n}$

$\Rightarrow R = R_{total} \times n = 0.80 \times 20 = 16\,\Omega$ ✓

(c) $R = \frac{\rho l}{A}$

$\Rightarrow A = \frac{\rho l}{R} = \frac{1.1 \times 10^{-6} \times 1.2}{16} = 8.25 \times 10^{-8}\,m^2$ ✓

(d) radius of each wire = $\sqrt{\frac{A}{\pi}} = \sqrt{\frac{8.25 \times 10^{-8}}{\pi}} = 1.6 \times 10^{-4}\,m$ ✓

Therefore, the diameter is about 0.32 mm so it is unlikely that the driver will see the wires in the rear windscreen ✓.

Question 25

Figure 5 shows a 12 kΩ potentiometer connected across a 5.0 V power supply of negligible internal resistance.

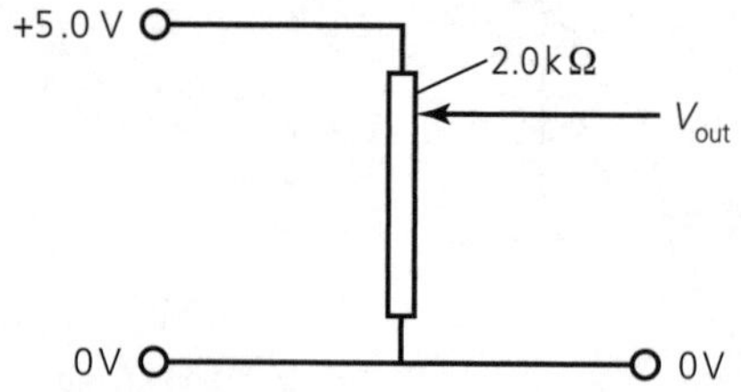

Figure 5

The potentiometer is set so that the resistance of the upper part is 2.0 kΩ.

(a) Calculate the output voltage. (1 mark)

(b) Explain what will happen as the sliding contact is moved down towards the bottom of the potentiometer resistor. (2 marks)

(c) **The slider is returned to the position shown and a load resistor of value 10 kΩ is connected across the output. Calculate the new output voltage.** (2 marks)

(d) **With the 10 kΩ resistor connected, it is required that the output voltage is 2.5 V. Show that the resistance of the top part of the potentiometer has to be about 4.3 kΩ for the output voltage to be 2.5 V.** (3 marks)

(Total 8 marks)

e Potential divider questions will sometimes ask for the effect of adding a load to the output, as this changes the effective resistance of the lower part of the potentiometer. The output voltage will reduce whenever a load resistor is added. When doing your calculations, always write down the formula you are going to use.

Answers

(a) The formula for a potential divider is:

$$V_{out} = \frac{R_2}{(R_1+R_2)} \times V$$

Substituting values:

$$V_{out} = \frac{10.0\times10^3}{10\times10^3+2.0\times10^3} \times 5.0 = 4.2\text{V} \checkmark$$

(b) As the slider is moved down the potentiometer resistor, the output voltage will become smaller ✓ in direct proportion to the remaining resistance ✓.

(c) The resistance of the lower part is now given by 10 kΩ in parallel with another 10 kΩ ✓. As the two resistors are the same, the total is 5.0 kΩ ✓. The output voltage is now:

$$V_{out} = \frac{5.0\times10^3}{(2.0\times10^3+5.0\times10^3)} \times 5.0 = 3.6\text{ V} \checkmark$$

(d) In order for the output voltage to be 2.5 V, the resistance of the bottom part must equal the resistance of the top part of the potentiometer ✓. If the top part is 4.3 kΩ, the bottom part has a resistance of 12 – 4.3 = 7.7 kΩ ✓.

Using the formula for resistors in parallel:

$$\frac{1}{R_{total}} = \left(\frac{1}{7.7\times10^3}\right)+\left(\frac{1}{10\times10^3}\right) = (1.3\times10^{-4}) + (1.0\times10^{-4}) = 2.3\times10^{-4}$$

$$\Rightarrow R_{total} = 4.3\text{ k}\Omega \checkmark$$

e You could do part (d) of this question by setting up a quadratic equation for R_2 and solving that, but it is not necessary to do it this way as you are given the value.

Question 26

Figure 6 shows how the resistance of a thermistor varies with temperature.

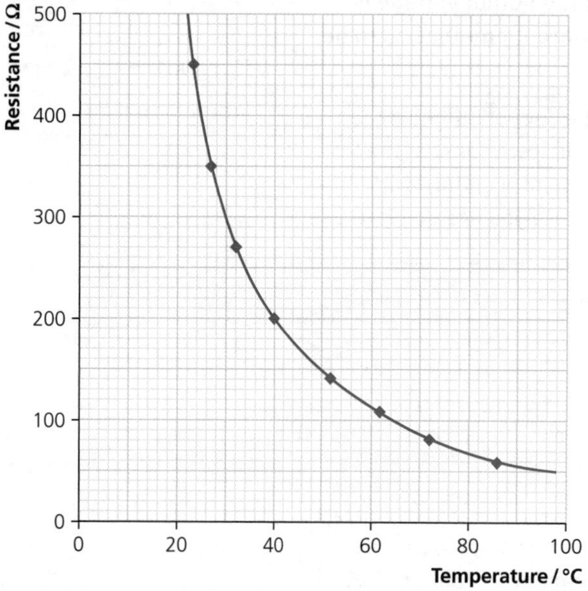

Figure 6

(a) **Describe how the resistance of the thermistor varies with temperature.** (2 marks)

(b) **Draw a suitable potential divider circuit so that the output voltage increases with increasing temperature.** (2 marks)

(c) **Explain whether there would be a greater change of output voltage with change of temperature at high or low temperatures.** (2 marks)

The supply voltage to the potential divider is 6.0 V.

(d) **Calculate the fixed resistor required to give an output voltage of 2.0 V at 25°C.** (2 marks)

(Total 8 marks)

ⓔ In part (a), you need to describe the pattern you see in the data. It is not enough simply to say that the resistance decreases with temperature. You need to describe how it changes – at a decreasing rate with temperature. Part (b) expects you to recall a potential divider circuit and be able to draw it correctly. Remember where the thermistor has to go for the output voltage to increase with increasing temperature. Part (c) requires you to interpret the data further and show that you understand that if the resistance changes less rapidly with temperature, so does the output voltage.

Answers

(a) The resistance decreases with temperature ✓. At low temperatures, small changes in temperature result in significant changes in resistance, but as the temperature increases the rate of change of resistance with temperature decreases ✓.

(b) See Figure 58 for the circuit diagram ✓. The thermistor should be shown as the resistor in the upper part of the circuit ✓.

(c) At low temperatures because the rate of change of resistance is greater ✓. The output voltage will also change more rapidly with temperature at lower temperatures ✓.

(d) At 25°C the resistance of the thermistor is 400 Ω ✓.

$$2.0\text{ V} = \frac{R_2}{(400 + R_2)} \times 6.0\text{ V} \Rightarrow R_2 = \frac{800}{4.0} = 200\,\Omega \checkmark$$

Question 27 (AS question)

A piece of wire 5.0 m long is connected to a resistance meter which reads 25.0 Ω. The diameter of the wire is measured in several places and found to be 0.11 mm.

The wire is then stretched by loading it with weights. The resistance is found to increase as the wire is stretched.

(a) Calculate the resistivity of the material used for the wire. (3 marks)

(b) Explain why the diameter of the wire is measured in several places. (2 marks)

(c) Suggest why the resistance of the wire is found to increase when it is stretched. (2 marks)

(Total 7 marks)

e This question is testing your understanding of resistivity and how changes to length and area will affect the resistance of a material. Part (a) requires you to calculate a cross-sectional area which can often result in errors if the calculation is not carefully done. In part (c), the command word is 'suggest' which means there is not necessarily a single right answer, but your reasoning is important.

Answers

(a) $\rho = \frac{RA}{l}$

$$A = \pi\left(\frac{d^2}{4}\right) = \pi \times \frac{(0.11 \times 10^{-3})^2}{4} = 9.5 \times 10^{-9}\text{ m}^2 \checkmark$$

$$\rho = \frac{RA}{l} = \frac{25 \times 9.5 \times 10^{-9}}{5.0} \checkmark = 4.8 \times 10^{-8}\,\Omega\text{m} \checkmark$$

(b) The wire may not be uniform along its length or may not be exactly round in cross-section ✓. By measuring in several places, an average value can be obtained and the uncertainty in the measurement estimated ✓.

(c) The length is increased and it is likely that the cross-sectional area of the wire is decreased, assuming the volume remains constant ✓. Therefore, from the equation:

$$R = \frac{\rho l}{A}$$

both changes will cause R to increase ✓.

Question 27 (A-level question)

A strain gauge is made from ten lengths of thin wire (see Figure 7). The wires are connected in series and each wire has a resistance of 120 Ω.

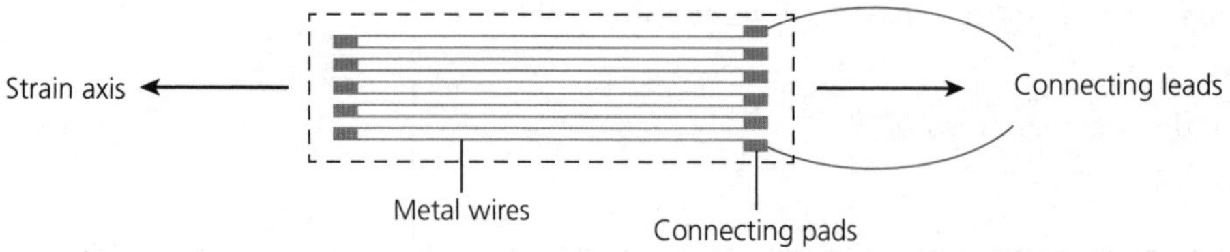

Figure 7

(a) **Calculate the total resistance of the strain gauge.** (1 mark)

The strain gauge is attached to something that will stretch and stretches with it in the direction shown. This changes the resistance of the wires.

You can assume that when the gauge is stretched, the volume, V, of each wire does not change — so that $V = A \times l$, where A is the cross-sectional area of the wire and l is the length.

(b) **Use this equation and the equation that links the resistance of the wire to its resistivity to show that $R \propto l^2$.** (2 marks)

(c) **The gauge is attached to a specimen that undergoes a strain of 0.005. Show that the resistance of the strain gauge changes by 1%.** (2 marks)

(d) **The Young modulus for the metal of the wire is 4.6×10^{10} Pa. Calculate the stress that will give a strain of 1%.** (2 marks)

(Total 7 marks)

e This question is using ideas of resistance and resistivity to test your understanding and your ability to apply your ideas. You may not have seen a strain gauge before but do not let a new situation put you off. The question is actually straightforward. However, it brings together ideas of resistance with materials and the Young modulus to test your understanding of both.

Answers

(a) For resistors in series, $R = 10 \times 120 = 1200\,\Omega$ ✓.

(b) $R = \frac{\rho l}{A}$ and $A = \frac{V}{l}$

$$\Rightarrow R = \frac{\rho \times l \times l}{V} = \frac{\rho}{V} \times l^2 \checkmark$$

Since both ρ and V are constant, $R \propto l^2$ ✓.

(c) $\frac{\Delta l}{l} = 0.005$ ✓

Therefore $\frac{\Delta R}{R} = 2 \times 0.005 = 0.01 = 1\%$ ✓

(d) Young modulus $= \frac{\text{stress}}{\text{strain}} \Rightarrow$ stress = Young modulus × strain ✓

$= 4.6 \times 10^{10} \times 0.01 = 4.6 \times 10^{8}$ Pa ✓

Question 28

A student sets up an experiment to measure the internal resistance and emf of a battery using the circuit shown in Figure 8.

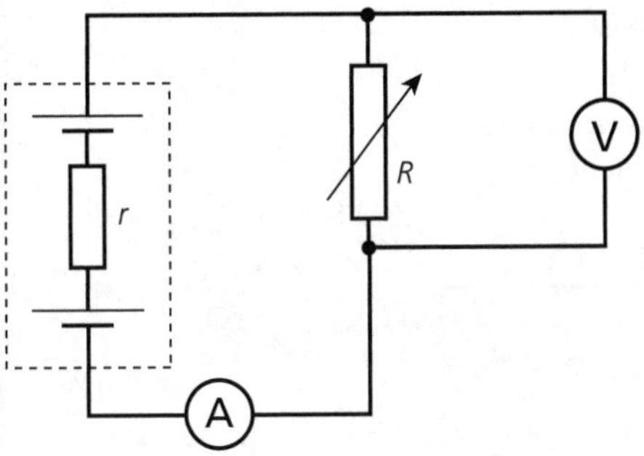

Figure 8

(a) Explain how the experiment is carried out and how the measurements are taken. (3 marks)

Table 2 shows the data obtained from the experiment.

p.d./V	5.5	4.1	3.0	2.0	1.2
Current/A	0.3	0.6	1.0	1.3	1.6

Table 2

(b) Plot the data on a copy of the grid in Figure 9. (2 marks)

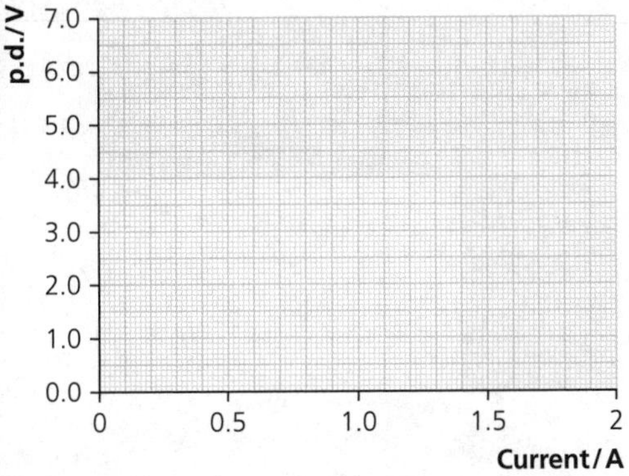

Figure 9

(c) By adding a suitable line, give a value for:

(i) The emf of the battery (1 mark)

(ii) The internal resistance of the battery (2 marks)

The battery consists of four identical cells in series.

(d) State the emf and internal resistance of each cell. (2 marks)

(e) State and explain any difficulties the student may have encountered with this experiment. (2 marks)

(Total 12 marks)

ⓔ This is the part of the paper that tests your knowledge of experimental techniques and what you know about required practicals. You should be able to gather data and use it to measure the internal resistance and emf of a cell or battery. Safety precautions, such as not allowing the cell to overheat, are also important to mention when necessary. Make sure you look at the number of marks available for each part of the question and write at least that number of separate points. You may find there are more possible points to make than there are marks available, but still write them all down to ensure you have covered everything.

Answers

(a) The value of the load resistor is changed in small steps ✓. After each change, the voltage across the load resistor ✓ and the current through it are measured and recorded ✓.

(b)

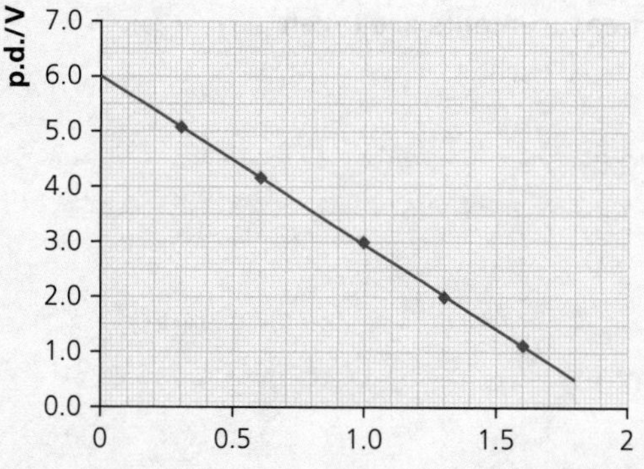

✓✓

(c) **(i)** The emf is the intercept on the *y*-axis, so is 6.0 V ✓.

(ii) The internal resistance is the gradient of the line ✓, so is:

$$\frac{6.0}{1.95} = 3.1\,\Omega \checkmark$$

(d) The emf of each cell is 1.5 V ✓. The internal resistance is:

$$\frac{3.1}{4} = 0.77\,\Omega \checkmark$$

(e) Care needs to be taken that the current does not get too big or that the larger currents are not allowed to flow for too long ✓. This could cause the cells to run down or to overheat ✓.

(Total for test paper 2: 70 marks)

Knowledge check answers

1 Scalar quantities: mass, length, distance, speed, energy, work done, temperature, amount of substance, time, volume, area
Vector quantities: displacement, velocity, acceleration, momentum, force, weight

2 $F_H = 40 \times \cos(30°) = 35\,N$
$F_V = 40 \times \sin(30°) = 20\,N$

3 The magnitude is 30 N at 274° to the north.

4 Taking moments about point B:
clockwise moment = $F_A \times 50\,m$
anticlockwise moments = $(10 \times 30) + (350 \times 25) = 9050\,kN\,m$
$F_A \times 50 = 9050\,kN\,m$
$F_A = 181\,kN$
$F_B = 179\,kN$ (You can check this by taking moments about point A.)

5 The centre of mass is always in the centre of the ball, so it remains at the same height above the flat surface.

6 $\Delta t = 3.0\,s$ therefore:
$$s = \frac{(15+8.0)}{2} \times 3.0 = 34.5\ m$$

7 Use $v^2 = u^2 + 2as$ to calculate the velocity when the ball hits the ground.
$v^2 = 2 \times 9.8 \times 1.0 \Rightarrow v = 4.4\,m\,s^{-1}$
To calculate the time taken use:
$$s = \frac{v+u}{2} \times t \Rightarrow t = \frac{1.0}{4.2/2} = 0.45s$$
Repeat the calculations for the ball rising. This time, the final velocity is zero and the initial velocity is unknown:
$v^2 = u^2 + 2as \Rightarrow u^2 = v^2 - (2 \times -9.8 \times 0.80)$
$\Rightarrow u = 4.0\,m\,s^{-1}$
Although u will now be upwards.
$$t = \frac{0.80}{4.0/2} = 0.40s$$
We can now sketch the graphs.

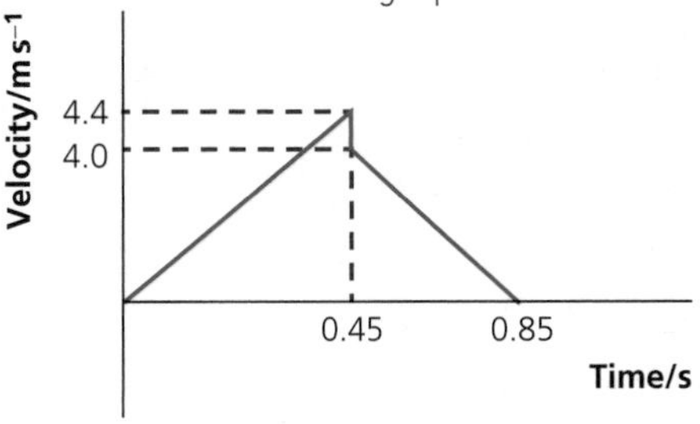

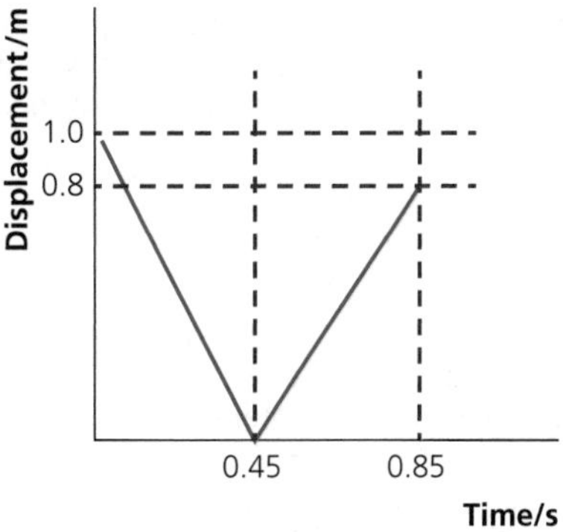

The gradient of the velocity–time graph will be $9.8\,m\,s^{-2}$ or $-9.8\,m\,s^{-2}$. The gradient of the displacement–time graph gives an average velocity of about $-2.2\,m\,s^{-1}$ as the ball falls and an average velocity of about $2\,m\,s^{-1}$ as the ball bounces back up again.

8 Use $s = ut + \frac{1}{2}at^2$:
$2.0 = (-3.0 \times t) + (\frac{1}{2} \times 9.8 \times t^2) \Rightarrow 4.9t^2 - 3.0t - 2.0 = 0$
This has to be solved for t using the formula for the solution of a quadratic equation, which gives $t = 1.0\,s$.

9 $a = \frac{F}{m} = \frac{300}{0.06} = 5000\,m\,s^{-2}$

10 **a** The four pairs of forces are:
- **i** The caravan is attracted towards the Earth with a force equal to its weight and the Earth is attracted to the caravan with the same force.
- **ii** The caravan pushes down on the ground with a force equal to its weight and the ground pushes back up on the caravan with the same force.
- **iii** The car pulls on the caravan with a force of 400 N and the caravan pulls back on the car with the same force.
- **iv** There is a frictional force backwards on the caravan of 100N and the caravan is pulling on the ground forwards with the same force.

b The acceleration is:
$$a = \frac{F}{m} = \frac{300}{500} = 0.600\,m\,s^{-2}$$

11 1 N is $1\,kg\,m\,s^{-2}$, therefore $1\,N\,s = 1\,kg\,m\,s^{-2} \times s = 1\,kg\,m\,s^{-1}$.

12 Momentum is $m \times v = 2 \times 0.5 = 1\,kg\,m\,s^{-1}$.

13 **a** The impulse is $\Delta mv = 900 \times 13 = 1.2 \times 10^4\,N\,s$.
b The average force is:
$$\frac{\text{impulse}}{\text{time}} = \frac{1.2 \times 10^4}{3.0} = 3.9 \times 10^3 N$$

14 Internal combustion engines get hot so most of the energy from the fuel is wasted as heat energy to the surroundings. This can be as much as 70% of the energy in the fuel.

15 gravitational potential energy gained = 5 × 9.8 × 2 = 98 J

16 kinetic energy = $\frac{1}{2} \times 60 \times 10^{-3} \times 40^2 = 48$ J

17 elastic strain energy = $\frac{1}{2} \times 5.0 \times 0.1 = 0.25$ J

18 The density of the heated air is less than that of the surrounding cooler air. This means that the total weight of the balloon and its contents is less than the weight of the cooler air it displaces.

19 The density of ice is less than that of water (about 90% that of water, especially salt water), so 90% of an iceberg displaces its own weight of water. This means that most of the iceberg is under water but some, about 10%, is above water.

20 a $F = k\Delta l \Rightarrow k = \frac{F}{\Delta l} = \frac{4.0}{5.0 \times 10^{-2}} = 80\ \text{Nm}^{-1}$

$\Delta l = \frac{F}{k} = \frac{9.5}{80} = 0.12\ \text{m} = 12\ \text{cm}$

b total length = 25 + 12 = 37 cm

21 1.3% = 0.013, therefore Δl = 0.013 × 3 = 0.039 m or 3.9 cm. The new length is therefore 3.039 m.

22

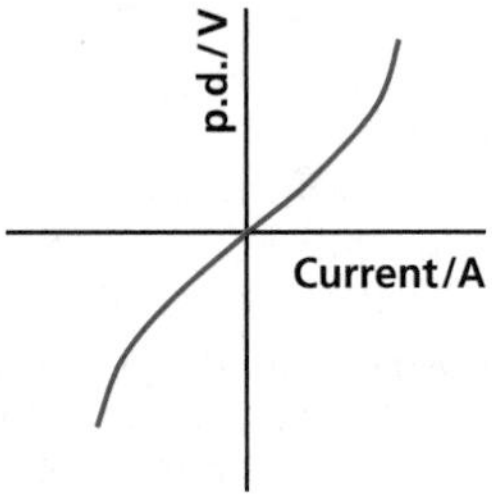

23 Using the defining equation for resistivity:

$\rho = \frac{RA}{l}$

We can substitute the units for the quantity:

unit for $\rho = \frac{\Omega\ \text{m}^2}{\text{m}} = \Omega\ \text{m}$

24 a −10°C
b 50°C
c 135°C
d 200°C

25

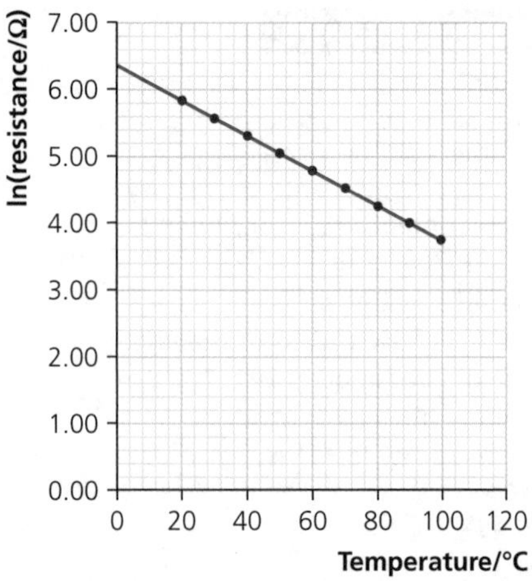

The intercept, ln R_0, is 6.35 so R_0 = 573 Ω.
k is 0.03°C^{-1}

26 25 Ω

27 $\frac{1}{R_{total}} = \frac{1}{R_1} + \frac{1}{R_2} + \frac{1}{R_3}$

$\Rightarrow \frac{1}{R_{total}} = \frac{1}{12} + \frac{1}{10} + \frac{1}{3} = \frac{62}{120}$

$\Rightarrow R_{total} = \frac{120}{62} = 1.9\ \Omega$

28 Three 18 Ω resistors in parallel have a total resistance of 6 Ω.
Four 20 Ω resistors in parallel have a total resistance of 5 Ω.
The two combinations in series is 6 Ω + 5 Ω = 11 Ω.

29 $P = I^2R \Rightarrow I^2 = \frac{3000}{17.8} = 169 \Rightarrow I = \sqrt{169} = 13.0$ A

30 a 6 × 1.5 = 9 V
b Six cells in parallel will still have a potential difference of 1.5 V across the arrangement.

31 $V_{out} = \frac{R_2}{R_1 + R_2} V_{in} = \frac{75}{75 + 25} \times 10 = 7.5$ V

32 $V_{out} = \frac{R_2}{R_1 + R_2} V_{in}$

$\Rightarrow V_{out} = \frac{2.2 \times 10^3}{(1.0 \times 10^3 + (2.2 \times 10^3)} \times 6.0 = 4.1$ V

33 total resistance in the circuit = 2.0 + 6.0 = 8.0 Ω.

$I = \frac{V}{R} = \frac{3.0}{8.0} = 0.38$ A

terminal potential difference = $I \times R$ = 0.38 × 6.0 = 2.3 V

Note: **bold** page numbers indicate defined terms.

Index